P9-BZS-849

Canadian Mathematics Competition

PROBLEMS
PROBLEMS
PROBLEMS
VOLUME 4

Canadian Mathematics Competition
Faculty of Mathematics
University of Waterloo
Waterloo, Ontario, Canada
1991

Published by
Waterloo Mathematics Foundation
University of Waterloo
Waterloo, Ontario, Canada
N2L 3G1

Telephone: (519) 885-1211, extension 3030
Fax: (519) 746-6592

Canadian Cataloguing in Publication Data

Main entry under title:

Problems, problems, problems

"Canadian Mathematics Competition".
ISBN 0-921418-04-3 (v. 4)

    1. Mathematics--Examinations, questions, etc.
I. Waterloo Mathematics Foundation. II. Canadian
Mathematics Competition.

QA139.P69 1988   510'.76   C88-090190-X

© 1991 Waterloo Mathematics Foundation
  University of Waterloo, Waterloo, Ontario, Canada

All rights reserved. No part of this publication may be
reproduced, stored in a retrieval system, or transmitted
in any form or by any means, electronic, mechanical,
photocopying, recording or otherwise, without the prior
written permission of the Waterloo Mathematics
Foundation.

Printed by Graphic Services, University of Waterloo

Introduction

The Canadian Mathematics Competition, which originated in 1963, is an annual national mathematics competition for students from Grade 7 to the senior secondary school level. The contests provide innovative and challenging problems for students with an aptitude for mathematics and an interest in testing their problem solving skills.

The Gauss Contest for Grade 7 and 8 students began on a local basis as a Grand Valley Mathematics Association project in the early 1970s and was offered on a national basis in 1974. Since 1985, separate contests have been provided for students in the two grades. Approximately 60 000 students now participate annually in the Gauss Contest, which is available in both English and French.

For many years, math teacher/coaches have used reprints of previous contests as a source of enrichment for their classrooms and to prepare students for writing the current year's contest. Since contests include questions involving many concepts with varying degrees of difficulty, these reprints are not ideal for either purpose. Therefore, in response to requests from teachers, we have compiled a series of Problems books that offer a ready source of problems for both classroom enrichment and contest preparation. *Problems Problems Problems – Volume 4* is the fourth in the series and is comprised of problems from previous Gauss and Pascal (Grade 9) Contests. Questions have been organized by topic and degree of difficulty. Half of the questions are presented in their original multiple choice format, and the remaining half have been rewritten to require full written solutions.

Classroom Enrichment

The mathematics curriculum guidelines at all levels have identified Problem Solving as the top priority. The best way to accomplish this goal is to integrate Problem Solving with teaching concepts. This means that Problem Solving should become a regular activity. Since the problems in this book have been organized by topic, it is a resource that can readily provide problems that match the curriculum topics. Feedback from teachers confirms that this process works. We would recommend that the full solution format be used for this purpose.

Contest Preparation

Preparation for contests is a rewarding enrichment activity and should be fun for students and teachers. It should occur over an extended period of the school year. It is very discouraging for students as their initial experience to encounter problems from up to 15 different areas as well as from average to challenging in degree of difficulty. Many students have been reluctant to participate in the Gauss Contest as a result of such an experience. We recommend that teachers use the "Topic Approach" for most of the contest preparation sessions. This enables the students to become comfortable with each area of mathematics and ensures that teachers base problems on familiar concepts. At a time closer to the contest date, after familiarity with all concepts in the course, a "simulation" of writing a contest is in order. This can be done by having the student work on contests from the preceding one or two years. A method of preparing for contests that focuses primarily on topics and culminates with work on one or two complete contests is the model we recommend.

We wish to thank those who assisted in the production of this book. Many teachers (elementary, secondary, and university) worked on the committees that produced these problems. Members of the Canadian Mathematics Competition executive: Ed Anderson, Lloyd Auckland, Larry Davidson, Ron Dunkley, Barry Ferguson and Ron Scoins contributed to the preparation of the book. We also thank Kimberley Parsons for the technical production of the text and diagrams, with assistance from Bonnie Findlay, Joanne Kursikowski and Betty Weber. We acknowledge the generous support of the University of Waterloo and our corporate sponsors.

The Competition applauds the many teachers who, through their interest and encouragement, help develop their students' interest in mathematics and their desire to work at developing their problem solving skills. We hope that this new problems book will provide students, teachers, parents and others with an opportunity to experience the joy of mathematics.

Canadian Mathematics Competition
Faculty of Mathematics
University of Waterloo
Waterloo, Ontario, Canada
February, 1991

Contents

* Topics indicated with a "I" will be continued in a future volume.

Contest References

Each question in the book has been given a reference number of the form "year-contest-question number". For example, 1988-G8-24 indicates question 24 from the 1988 Grade 8 Gauss Contest. The contest abbreviations are: G7 - Grade 7 Gauss Contest, G8 - Grade 8 Gauss Contest, G - Gauss Contest (prior to 1985, students in Grades 7 and 8 wrote the same paper), P - Grade 9 Pascal Contest, C - Grade 10 Cayley Contest and J - Junior (prior to 1981, the Pascal, Cayley and Fermat Contests were combined into one paper called the Junior Mathematics Contest).

Questions

A circus clown buys balloons at $1.44 per dozen and sells them for 20 cents each. What will be his profit on a day when he sells 20 dozen balloons?

Decimals

Multiple Choice Questions

1985-G7-9
1. One and twenty-four hundredths is
    (A) 0.124   (B) 1.024   (C) 1.24   (D) 124.00   (E) 12 400

1990-G8-1
2. The value of $25 \div 0.05$ is
    (A) 5000   (B) 500   (C) 50   (D) 5   (E) 1.25

1987-G7-1
3. $0.2 \times 0.2 \times 0.2$ equals
    (A) 0.6   (B) 0.08   (C) 0.8   (D) 0.008   (E) 0.006

1989-G7-2

4. The value of $2 + \frac{7}{100} + \frac{3}{1000}$ may be expressed as

(A) 2.01   (B) 2.073   (C) 2.10   (D) 2.703   (E) 2.73

1982-P-2

5. $\frac{10}{0.1} - 10$ is equal to

(A) 99   (B) 90   (C) –90   (D) –9   (E) 9

1986-P-6

6. Of the following, the closest approximation to $0.435 \div 0.0821$ is

(A) 0.02   (B) 0.2   (C) 0.5   (D) 5   (E) 50

1985-P-12

7. The integer closest to $\sqrt{\frac{60.1}{0.99} + 3.95}$ is

(A) 3   (B) 8   (C) 9   (D) 25   (E) 64

1975-G-2

8. The result of multiplying the difference between 9.2 and 8.679 by 0.003 is

(A) 0.25701   (B) 0.0025701   (C) 0.1563   (D) 0.01563   (E) 0.001563

1986-P-5

9. Of the five numbers, 1.1, 1.01, 1.001, 1.0101, 1.00101, the one that is the least is

(A) 1.1   (B) 1.01   (C) 1.001   (D) 1.0101   (E) 1.00101

1987-G8-9

10. Given that $\frac{1}{3} = 0.\overline{3}$ and $\frac{1}{2} = 0.5$, the value of $\frac{1}{2} + \frac{1}{3}$ is

(A) 0.8   (B) $0.5\overline{3}$ (C) $0.\overline{35}$ (D) $0.8\overline{3}$ (E) $0.\overline{8}$

1980-J-2

11. The second largest number in the set $\{0.3, 0.9, 0.18, 0.27, 0.081\}$ is

(A) 0.3   (B) 0.9   (C) 0.18   (D) 0.27   (E) 0.081

1976-J-7

12. If $A = \frac{0.1}{0.5}$, $B = \frac{0.5}{1}$, and $C = \frac{1}{0.5}$, then, in order of magnitude,

(A) $A > B > C$ (B) $B > A > C$ (C) $C > A > B$

(D) $A > C > B$ (E) $C > B > A$

1978-J-3

13. $\frac{(0.3)^3}{0.9}$ equals

(A) 3   (B) 1   (C) 0.3   (D) 0.03   (E) 0.003

1974-J-6

14. If $P = 0.25$, $Q = (0.25)^2$, and $R = \sqrt{0.25}$, then

(A) $P > Q > R$ (B) $Q > P > R$ (C) $R > Q > P$

(D) $R > P > Q$ (E) $Q > R > P$

1983-P-10

15. $\left[0.1 + \frac{1}{0.1}\right]^2$ equals

(A) 100.01   (B) 12.1   (C) 102.01   (D) 1.21   (E) 111.1

1971-J-13

16. If the numbers 0.3, $0.\dot{3}$, $(0.\dot{3})^2$, $\frac{1}{0.3}$, and $\frac{1}{0.\dot{3}}$ are arranged in order of magnitude, the middle number is

(A) 0.3 (B) $0.\dot{3}$ (C) $(0.\dot{3})^2$ (D) $\frac{1}{0.3}$ (E) $\frac{1}{0.\dot{3}}$

Full Solution Questions

1973-G-3

1. Find the sum of 2.0063 + 1.532 + 0.28.

1909-G0-1

2. Find the value of 6.9 − 4.91.

1985-G7-2

3. What is the sum of 0.48, 10.2, 0.03, and 8?

1990-G7-1

4. Find the value of 0.2 ÷ 0.4.

1984-P-1

5. What is the quotient when 0.1 is divided by 0.02?

1981-J-1

6. Find the value of 23.1 ÷ 0.11.

1984-C-1

7. What is the quotient when 0.01 is divided by 0.002?

1977-G-2

8. Find the number obtained when the difference between 14.2 and 1.69 is divided by 0.03.

1974-G-2

9. Express $\frac{1}{7}$ as a decimal fraction.

1982-G-8

10. Find the value of $(0.1)^2 - (0.1)^3$.

1980-G-15

11. What is the value of $\frac{a}{b} \times \frac{b}{a} - a$ if $a = 1.41$ and $b = 1.73$?

1981-G-15

12. A circus clown buys balloons at $1.44 per dozen and sells them for 20 cents each. What will be his profit on a day when he sells 20 dozen balloons?

1981-G-12

13. If $x = 0.3$, find the value of $\frac{1}{x}$.

1980-J-10

14. Four holes are to be drilled along the centre line of a strip of metal so that their centres are 2.25 cm apart. The centres of the two end holes are to be 3.35 cm from their corresponding ends. What length must the strip of metal be?

1983-G-14

15. Company *A* rents cars for $11.00 per day plus 5¢ per km. Company *B* rents cars for $14.00 per day plus 4¢ per km. What is the difference in total rental charges on a trip of 1550 km, if the trip takes 2 days?

1982-P-22

16. Cylindrical rods of metal of diameter 0.25 cm are bent to form circular links of a chain. If each link has an outer diameter of 2 cm, what is the length of a 100-link chain when pulled taut?

A student using an electronic calculator mistakenly multiplies by 10 instead of dividing by 10. The incorrect answer on display is 600. What is the correct answer?

Operations with Integers - I

Multiple Choice Questions

1976-G-1
1. The value of $11 - 3(5 - 2)$ is

(A) 24   (B) 2   (C) –2   (D) 38   (E) –5

1978-G-1
2. $\left(6 + 5 \times 4^2\right) \div 2$ equals

(A) 203   (B) 88   (C) 23   (D) 166   (E) 43

1987-G7-2
3. The value of $12 + 6 \div 3 \times 2 - 1$ is

(A) 15   (B) 11   (C) 35   (D) 12   (E) 14

1980-G-3

4. The answer given by the following flowchart is

$$\text{Start} \rightarrow 13 \rightarrow +7 \rightarrow \div 5 \rightarrow -1 \rightarrow \text{answer} \rightarrow \text{Stop}$$

(A) 3.0   (B) 4.0   (C) 5.0   (D) 13.4   (E) 14.75

1978-G-2

5. −7 equals
   (A) $16 - 9$ (B) $(3 - 4)(3 + 4)$ (C) $(4 + 3)(4 - 3)$
   (D) $-4 + 11$ (E) $\sqrt{49}$

1980-G-2

6. The number $5 \times 10^5 + 5 \times 10^3 + 5 \times 10^2 + 5$ equals
   (A) 5555   (B) 55 505   (C) 50 555   (D) 505 505   (E) 5555×10^{10}

1986-G7-3

7. In the statement $6 \ast 8 \oplus 2 = 10$, the operations $\ast$ and $\oplus$ respectively represent
   (A) −, ×   (B) ×, +   (C) +, ×   (D) ×, ÷   (E) +, ÷

1983-G-6

8. The value of $\sqrt{100 - 36}$ is
   (A) 2   (B) 4   (C) 64   (D) $\sqrt{8}$ (E) 8

1985-G-7

9. If $a = 2$, then $4a^3$ is equal to
   (A) 24   (B) 32   (C) 64   (D) 128   (E) 512

1981-G-8

10. A student using an electronic calculator mistakenly multiplies by 10 instead of dividing by 10. The incorrect answer on display is 600. The correct answer is
    (A) 0.6   (B) 6   (C) 60   (D) 6 000   (E) 60 000

1975-G-12

11. If $x = 2$ and $y = -3$, the value of $x^3 - y^3$ is
    (A) −3   (B) 15   (C) 35   (D) −19   (E) −1

1979-G-20

12. The expression $4n - 6$ is evaluated for $n = 0, 1, 2$, and 3. The sum of the four resulting numbers is

   (A) 0   (B) –4   (C) 2   (D) 6   (E) 16

Full Solution Questions

1974-G-1

1. Find the value of $6 + 5(7 - 3) \div 2$.

1980-G-1

2. Find the value of $12 + 4(3 - 7)$.

1984-G-4

3. If $x = 4$, find the value of $3x^2 + 7$.

1975-G-5

4. If $a = 2$, $b = 3$, and $c = 4$, find the value of bc^a.

1982-G-6

5. Find the simplified form of $3 \times 10^5 + 4 \times 10^3 + 7 \times 10^2 + 5$.

1984-G-6

6. Find the value of $-1^2 - 1^3$.

1977-G-8

7. Find the value of $3^2 + 4^3 + 2^4$.

1979-G-14

8. If $a = 2$ and $b = 3$, find the value of $(a^b)^2$.

1974-G-16

9. If $x = 2$ and $y = 3$, find the value of $-x^2 + (-y)^3$.

1979-G-16

10. Find the value of $x + 2y$, if $x = 7$ and $xy = 91$.

1988-G8-19

11. If a and b are integers, then $a^2 - b^2 = (a + b)(a - b)$. Find the value of $2501^2 - 2500^2$.

1978-G-21

12. The variable n in the expression $3 + 2n$ is replaced in succession by 1, 2, 3, and 4. Find the sum of the resulting numbers.

A ski shop offered a 25% discount on a pair of skis that originally sold for $90.00. The new price was then reduced by 10%. What was the final sale price?

Percentages - I

Multiple Choice Questions

1971 J-1
1. 1000% of 2 equals
   (A) 2000   (B) 1002   (C) 200   (D) 20   (E) 0.002

1980-G-8
2. 0.75% of 264 is
   (A) 352   (B) 198   (C) 3.52   (D) 1.98   (E) 0.198

1988-G7-3
3. Heidi purchases a calculator priced at $8.80. If the sales tax is 5%, the total cost, in dollars, is
   (A) 0.44   (B) 8.36   (C) 9.20   (D) 9.24   (E) 13.20

1986-G7-13

4. Cherie has written five tests this year. Her marks were $\frac{8}{10}, \frac{47}{50}, \frac{23}{25}, \frac{60}{75}$, and 85%. The
    test on which she did best was the one on which she scored

    (A) $\frac{8}{10}$ (B) $\frac{47}{50}$ (C) $\frac{23}{25}$ (D) $\frac{60}{75}$ (E) 85%

1980-G-14

5. A ski shop offered a 25% discount on a pair of skis that originally sold for $90.00.
    The new price was then reduced by 10%. The final sale price was

    (A) $31.50   (B) $55.00   (C) $81.00   (D) $58.50   (E) $60.75

1979-G-21

6. A man borrowed $3500 and a year later paid back the loan plus interest with a cheque
    for $4200. The annual rate of interest, in percent, paid for the loan was

    (A) 700   (B) 83.3   (C) 20   (D) 120   (E) 16.6

1989-G8-15

7. Kelli's Kleeners raised the price of dry cleaning a jacket from $4.00 to $5.00. The
    same percentage increase was applied to the price of dry cleaning a coat. The old cost
    of dry cleaning a coat was $10.00. The new cost, in dollars, of dry cleaning a coat
    will be

    (A) 2.00   (B) 2.50   (C) 11.00   (D) 12.00   (E) 12.50

1989-G7-14

8. The Canadian dollar was recently equivalent in value to $0.80 in American currency.
    The value of one American dollar in Canadian currency at that time was

    (A) $1.20   (B) $1.25   (C) $1.80   (D) $1.44   (E) $1.64

1984-F-11

9. A team's record is 20 wins and 25 losses. To qualify for the playoffs a team must win
    60% of its games played. The number of wins of the remaining 15 games necessary
    for the team to qualify is

    (A) 4   (B) 10   (C) 12   (D) 15   (E) impossible
                                                               to achieve

1991-P-14

10. In a recent election with three candidates, Mrs. Jones received 10 575 votes, Mr. Smith
    received 7990 votes, and Mr. Green received 2585 votes. If 90% of those eligible to
    vote did so, the number of eligible voters was

    (A) 19 035   (B) 23 265   (C) 23 500   (D) 21 150   (E) 49 572

1976-G-26

11. On a $10.00 purchase, Tom was offered 3 successive discounts of 20%, 10%, and 5% in any order he wished. He selected the discounts in the order 5%, 10%, and 20%. Which of the following order of discounts would have been better for him?
    (A) 20, 10, 5   (B) 20, 5, 10   (C) 5, 20, 10   (D) 10, 20, 5   (E) none of these

1974-J-7

12. In each of three successive years, the cost of living increases by 10%. The percentage increase in the three years is
    (A) 30   (B) 130   (C) 33.1   (D) 33   (E) 133.1

1972-J-9

13. A man has a rectangular patio in his garden. He decides to enlarge it by increasing both length and width by 10%. The percentage increase in area is
    (A) 10   (B) 20   (C) 21   (D) 40   (E) 121

Full Solution Questions

1979-G-3

1. Find 500% of 2.

1984-G-9

2. The yearly interest paid on a loan of $1200 is $180. What is the annual rate of interest, expressed as a percent?

1985-G8-9

3. In playing Space Invaders, Janet shot down 12 of the 25 Invaders with 50 shots. One successful shot destroys one Invader. What percent of Janet's shots hit Invaders?

1980-J-7

4. If 10% of x is equal to 25% of 16, what is the value of x?

1975-G-13

5. When 4131 people attended a concert, the concert hall was 90% full. What is the capacity of the hall?

1982-P-10

6. In the latest We-All-Win Lottery Draw, 0.08% of the tickets sold won prizes. How many tickets were sold if two prizes were won?

1978-G-10

7. A Big McBurger is 30% beef, 30% cereal, 20% water, and 20% ingredients untouched by human hands. If one pound equals 16 ounces, determine the water content, in ounces, of a $\frac{1}{4}$ pound Big McBurger.

1975-G-20

8. The cost of a can of wax, including 5% sales tax, is $1.20. If the price of a can of wax, without sales tax, is reduced to 70% of its original cost, what is the new price before the tax is added?

1990-G8-17

9. Sam's age is 125% of Mary's age. Mary's age is $p\%$ of Sam's age. What is the value of p?

1977-G-23

10. Harry Wirks earns a salary of $360 per week for a 44 hour week. His weekly salary is increased by 10% and his hours are reduced by 10%. Calculate his new hourly salary.

1986-G7-22

11. On a test of 30 questions, Sue had 50% more right answers than she had wrong answers. Each answer was either right or wrong. How many questions did she answer correctly?

1984-C-20

12. Mr. Afton has an income which is five-eights of Miss Benson's. Mr. Afton's expenses are one-half those of Miss Benson, and Mr. Afton saves 40% of his income. What percentage of her income does Miss Benson save?

1991-F-18

13. A rectangular section was cut from a rectangular block as shown in the diagram. Determine the percentage decrease in the surface area.

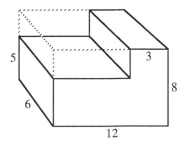

During a football game, Joe Leggit punted the ball three times. His longest kick was 43 m and the three punts averaged 37 metres. If the other two punts were the same length, find the distance, in metres, that each travelled.

Averages

Multiple Choice Questions

1986-G7-2

1. The average of 6.2 and 0.62 is

   (A) 3.069   (B) 3.131   (C) 3.41   (D) 3.72   (E) 6.2

1977-J-3

2. The average of $\frac{1}{2}$, $\frac{2}{3}$, and $\frac{3}{4}$ is

   (A) $\frac{2}{3}$ (B) $\frac{23}{36}$ (C) $\frac{23}{12}$ (D) $\frac{23}{24}$ (E) none of these

1985-G7-11

3. The average of the five numbers 4.9, 3.1, 7.7, 0.5, and 9.3 is

(A) 0.5   (B) 5.0   (C) 5.1   (D) 6.02   (E) 6.25

1978-G-11

4. The average of $\frac{2}{3}$, 0.7, and $\frac{55}{100}$ is

(A) $\frac{115}{20}$ (B) $1\frac{11}{12}$ (C) $1\frac{3}{4}$ (D) $\frac{23}{36}$ (E) $1\frac{7}{12}$

1985-F-2

5. The number halfway between $\frac{1}{8}$ and $\frac{7}{12}$ is

(A) $\frac{2}{5}$ (B) $\frac{1}{2}$ (C) $\frac{1}{3}$ (D) $\frac{11}{48}$ (E) $\frac{17}{48}$

1991-P-4

6. The average of two numbers is 5. If one of the numbers is –8, then the other number is

(A) 2   (B) 9   (C) 13   (D) 18   (E) 26

1975-G-11

7. Five boys wrote a mathematics test. The average mark was 68. If the marks of four boys were 75, 62, 84, and 53, the mark of the fifth boy was

(A) 66   (B) 68   (C) 76   (D) 68.5   (E) 56

1989-G7-8

8. The average of three numbers is 10. If one of the numbers is 5, the sum of the remaining two numbers is

(A) 10   (B) 15   (C) 20   (D) 25   (E) 30

1990-G7-12

9. During March, Sally bowled 10 games with an average score of 190. During April, she bowled four games with an average score of 162. Over the two month period, her average score was

(A) 100   (B) 170   (C) 175   (D) 176   (E) 182

1981-G-17

10. At the end of the season, the standings of the teams in a school soccer league were

Team	Games Played	Wins	Losses	Ties	Goals For	Goals Against	Points
Drillers	12	8	3		60	36	
Blizzard	12	7	3		51	41	
Kickers	12	4	4		48	48	
Flames	12	3	7		39	50	
White Caps	12	3	8		37	60	

Using information from the table, the average number of goals scored in each of the games played by the Drillers was

(A) 12　　　(B) 7.5　　　(C) 6　　　(D) 8　　　(E) 3

1982-P-3

11. The average of a set of integers is 6. The sum of the integers is 18. The number of integers in the set is

(A) 3　　　(B) 108　　　(C) 12　　　(D) 6　　　(E) none of these

1981-J-6

12. The regular price of a popsicle is 10 cents and a special sale price for Mondays is 5 cents. If Karen bought 15 popsicles on Saturday and 10 on Monday, then the average price she paid for each popsicle, in cents, was

(A) 7　　　(B) 7.5　　　(C) 8　　　(D) 8.5　　　(E) none of these

1968-J-8

13. A class of 20 students averaged 66% on an examination; another class of 30 students averaged 56%. The average percentage for all students was

(A) 58　　　(B) 62　　　(C) 61　　　(D) 59　　　(E) none of these

1988-G7-19

14. When Friedrich wrote the Gauss Contest, he averaged 1 minute per question on the 10 questions in Part A, 2 minutes per question on the 10 questions in Part B, and 6 minutes per question on the 5 questions in Part C. The average time he spent on each question in the entire contest, in minutes, was

(A) $\frac{12}{5}$　　　(B) $\frac{9}{25}$　　　(C) $\frac{25}{9}$　　　(D) $\frac{20}{3}$　　　(E) 20

1981-G-21

15. The average mark on a test for six students was calculated to be 84. One student's mark had been mistakenly counted as an 86 rather than the correct mark of 68. The correct average for these six students is

   (A) 87   (B) 83   (C) 82   (D) 81   (E) 78

1974-J-15

16. If m pens are bought at n dollars each, and n pens at m dollars each, then the average cost per pen, in dollars, is

   (A) mn (B) $\frac{2mn}{m+n}$ (C) $\frac{m+n}{2}$ (D) 1   (E) $\frac{m^2n^2}{2}$

1984-P-21

17. In her latest game, Mary bowled 199 and raised her average from 177 to 178. To raise her average to 179 with the next game, she must bowl

   (A) 179   (B) 180   (C) 199   (D) 200   (E) 201

1987-C-20

18. In a group of men and women, the average age is 31. If the men's ages average 35 years and the women's ages average 25, then the ratio of the number of men to the number of women is

   (A) 5 : 7   (B) 7 : 5   (C) 2 : 1   (D) 4 : 3   (E) 3 : 2

Full Solution Questions

1979-G-1

1. What is the average of 6, 15, and 45?

1980-G-9

2. On ten different tests, a student obtained the marks 5, 4, 7, 6, 8, 8, 8, 9, 7, and 6. What was her average mark?

1979-G-1

3. What is the average of $\frac{1}{2}$ and $\frac{3}{4}$?

1982-G-9

4. Find the average of the even numbers greater than 1 and less than 15.

1985-G8-11

5. If the average of the five numbers 4.9, 3.1, 7.7, k, and 9.3 is 5.1, determine the value of k.

1986-G7-19

6. In a set of five numbers, the average of the first two numbers is 10, and the average of the last three is 15. What is the average of all five numbers?

1978-G-15

7. A class of thirty students had an average mark of 68 on a mathematics test. Another class of 25 students had an average mark of 70 on the same test. What was the average mark for all the students?

1979-J-5

8. The average of two numbers is 7. When a third number is included, the average of the three numbers is 8. What is the third number?

1980-J-3

9. The average of –3 and a second number is 2. What is the second number?

1986-P-16

10. The average of a set of 10 numbers is 20. If one of the numbers is removed from the set, the average of the remaining numbers is 19. What number was removed?

1990-G8-12

11. A teacher recorded the test marks for a class of 23 students. Using these recorded marks, the average was calculated to be 72. Pierre's mark of 86 was incorrectly recorded as 36. What was the correct average for the test?

1983-P-13

12. In a competition, the average score of Pat's first four games was 6.5; the average of her next five games was 6.4. If she scored 9 on her tenth game, what was her overall average?

1971-J-12

13. Dullard Academy served 2068 dull lunches from Monday to Thursday inclusive. Given that the daily average for the five day week was 516 lunches, how many dull lunches were served on Friday?

1984-G-11

14. Bruns Wick, a bowler, obtained a total score in three games of 570. His average per game on these games was 9 below his previous average. What was his average before these three games?

1988-G7-24

15. A set of positive integers, each of which is different, has a sum of 329 and an average of 47. If one of the integers is 97, then what is the largest possible integer that could appear in the set?

1983-G-20

16. During a football game, Joe Leggit punted the ball three times. His longest kick was 43 metres and the three punts averaged 37 metres. If the other two punts were the same length, find the distance, in metres, that each travelled.

1987-P-13

17. The average of five consecutive integers is 10. What is the sum of the smallest and the largest of these five integers?

1991-C-19

18. Sanji receives a set of four marks. If the average of the first two marks is 50, the average of the second and third is 75, and the average of the third and fourth is 70, then what is the average of the first and fourth?

John has 400 spaghetti strands, each 15 cm long, on his lunch plate. If he joined them end to end (using sauce as glue) to form one long strand, what would the length of his lunch be?

Word Problems - I

Multiple Choice Questions

1980-G-6

1. John has 400 spaghetti strands, each 15 cm long, on his lunch plate. If he joined them end to end (*using sauce as glue*) to form one long strand, the length of his lunch would be

   (A) 6 km   (B) 60 m   (C) 600 cm   (D) 6 000 mm   (E) 60 000 cm

1983-G-9

2. In each hour of running, Bill Rodgers uses up 600 calories. In 1980 he won the Boston Marathon in 2 hours and 12 minutes. The number of calories he burned while running the race in this time was

   (A) 1440   (B) 1320   (C) 1272   (D) 1212   (E) 1140

1988-G7-6

3. From Monday to Friday, John sleeps 6 hours each night. On the remaining two nights, he gets half as much sleep as he gets for the first five nights. The total number of hours of sleep he gets in the full week is

(A) 75   (B) 45   (C) 42   (D) 36   (E) 33

1977-G-5

4. A number which is 7 less than twice the square root of 81 is

(A) 13 115   (B) 11   (C) 2   (D) 4   (E) 25

1976-G-19

5. Three consecutive even integers have the property that three times the smallest is equal to the sum of the other two. The smallest of the three integers is

(A) 4   (B) 3   (C) 8   (D) 6   (E) none of these

1989-G7-7

6. A school requires 1200 permission forms. Three of these forms can be printed on one sheet of paper. If it costs 4 cents to print each sheet, the total cost, in dollars, of printing the required forms is

(A) 12   (B) 16   (C) 48   (D) 100   (E) 1600

1978-G-6

7. Five dozen oranges were purchased at $1.32 per dozen and sold at 3 oranges for 35 cents. The total profit was

(A) $0.70   (B) $7.00   (C) $0.60   (D) $0.40   (E) $0.80

1990-G7-13

8. Pat, Dale, and Chris ate a 12-slice pizza. Pat ate 5 slices, Dale ate 4 slices, and Chris ate 3 slices. If the cost of Dale's share of the pizza was $3.40, then the cost of Pat's share, in dollars, was

(A) 2.72   (B) 3.70   (C) 4.08   (D) 4.25   (E) 10.20

1985-G7-22

9. When 16 litres are added to a gas tank which is $\frac{1}{2}$ full, the tank is $\frac{2}{3}$ full. The capacity of the tank, in litres, is

(A) 24   (B) 32   (C) 64   (D) $\frac{64}{3}$ (E) 96

1987-G7-13

10. A bus pass costs $30 per month. Without a pass, each ride costs $0.50. In a month, the fewest number of times a person with a bus pass must ride the bus to save money is

(A) 61   (B) 15   (C) 30   (D) 59   (E) 31

1975-G-16

11. Fred has 17 coins with a total value of 76 cents. The coins are nickels, dimes, and pennies. He has 5 more nickels than dimes and twice as many pennies as dimes. The number of nickels is

(A) 6   (B) 7   (C) 8   (D) 9   (E) none of these

1987-G7-24

12. Arin and Bob together have $1.35. Arin has only nickels while Bob has only dimes. Arin has six more coins than Bob. The number of coins possessed by the two of them together is

(A) 17   (B) 18   (C) 19   (D) 20   (E) 21

1975-G-24

13. A train 1000 metres long travels through a 3000 metre tunnel. If 30 seconds elapse from the time the last car enters the tunnel until the time when the engine emerges from the other end, the speed of the train, in metres per second, is

(A) $\frac{100}{3}$ (B) $\frac{200}{3}$ (C) 100   (D) 1000   (E) $\frac{400}{3}$

1985-G7-23

14. To make concrete, mix 4 shovels of stone, 2 shovels of sand, and 1 shovel of cement. The number of shovels of stone required to make 350 shovels of concrete is

(A) 200   (B) 150   (C) 100   (D) 87.5   (E) 50

Full Solution Questions

1986-G7-6

1. A doctor prescribed pills as follows: four red pills each day for five days, three orange pills each day for four days, two yellow pills each day for three days, and one green pill each day for two days. If each pill costs 50¢, find the total cost of the pills.

1986-G7-4

2. When 62 is divided by a certain number, the quotient is 7 and the remainder is 6. Find the number.

1974-G-7

3. A number N is doubled and then increased by 5. When this quantity is doubled, the result is 38. Find the value of N.

1989-G7-15

4. A glass is full of milk. The total weight is 370 g. When the glass is half full of milk, the weight is 290 g. Find the weight of the glass.

1983-G-4

5. A lady buys six dozen apples at $1.32 a dozen and sells each apple for 20¢. Find her profit.

1990-G7-18

6. Mary buys gumballs at 4 for 15¢ and sells them at 3 for 15¢. Find the number of gumballs Mary must sell to make a profit of $3.00.

1989-G7-9

7. Anne bought a soccer ball for $24.00. She sold it to Bill for $\frac{1}{6}$ less than she paid for it. Bill sold it to Cathy for $\frac{1}{5}$ less than he paid for it. Cathy sold it to Dave for $\frac{1}{4}$ less than she paid for it. Find the price that Dave paid for the ball.

1976-G-12

8. 900 people attended a dance. The cost of admission was $2.00 per person or $3.50 per couple. Twice as many $2.00 tickets as $3.50 tickets were sold. Find the amount of money obtained from ticket sales.

1982-G-22

9. Four students share $100. Al and Bob receive $\frac{1}{10}$ and $\frac{1}{5}$ of the total, respectively. Carl receives the average of what Al and Bob got. If Dave collects the remaining money, determine how much his share is.

1987-G8-13

10. An organization sent out a monthly newsletter to each of its 4000 members. When the cost of postage was increased from 32¢ a letter to 34¢ a letter, the organization decided to issue only 10 newsletters each year. Find the yearly savings in postage that resulted from this decision.

1990-G7-7

11. A 1600-seat theatre is divided into three sections: Orchestra, Mezzanine, and Balcony. There are 540 seats in the Orchestra section. There are 300 more seats in the Mezzanine than there are in the Balcony. Find the number of seats in the Mezzanine.

1984-G-19

12. John has 9 coins in his pocket. Each coin is worth less than $1.00. The coins represent four different denominations and include exactly one fifty-cent piece and three nickels. Find the largest amount he could have.

1984-G-25

13. Joe has some spheres, each of which weighs the same. He also has some cubes, each of which weighs the same. He discovered that 4 spheres and 3 cubes weigh 37 g and that 3 spheres and 4 cubes weigh 33 g. Find the combined weight, in grams, of one sphere and one cube.

1978-G-20

14. A motorcycle and a truck left a roadside diner at the same time. After travelling in the same direction for one and one-quarter hours, the motorcycle had travelled 25 kilometres farther than the truck. If the average speed of the motorcycle was 60 kilometres per hour, find the average speed of the truck.

A tree of height 45 m casts a shadow of 30 m. What is the height, in metres, of a tree casting a 28 m shadow?

Ratios - I

Multiple Choice Questions

1986-G7-15
1. If $\frac{3}{4}$ of a number is 12, then $\frac{3}{2}$ of the same number is

   (A) 36   (B) 24   (C) 18   (D) $13\frac{1}{2}$ (E) 12

1985-G8-5
2. A railway engine is 12 m long. To build a model railway to $\frac{1}{100}$ scale, the length of the model engine, in cm, must be

   (A) 0.012   (B) 0.12   (C) 1.2   (D) 12   (E) 120

25

1974-G-15

3. Two numbers are in the ratio of 7 : 3. The difference of the two numbers is 24. The larger number is

(A) 34   (B) 42   (C) 18   (D) 96   (E) 56

1984-P-7

4. If 50 is divided into three parts in the ratio 1 : 3 : 6, then the middle part is

(A) 5   (B) 15   (C) $\frac{50}{3}$ (D) 30   (E) 3

1974-G-9

5. A boy weighs 90 pounds and a girl weighs 74 pounds. The ratio of the girl's weight to their combined weight is

(A) 37 : 82   (B) 82 : 37   (C) 45 : 82   (D) 37 : 45   (E) 82 : 45

1990-G7-11

6. Eight centimetres of snow contain as much water as 0.75 cm of rain. Inuvik receives about 425 cm of snow each year. If the snow fell as rain, the number of centimetres would be approximately

(A) 4   (B) 6   (C) 36   (D) 40   (E) 300

1986-G8-20

7. If the total cost of P articles is Q dollars, then the cost, in dollars, of R articles of the same type is

(A) PQR (B) $\frac{P}{QR}$ (C) $\frac{PR}{Q}$ (D) $\frac{QR}{P}$ (E) $\frac{R}{PQ}$

1979-G-26

8. A day is divided into 10 new-hours, each new-hour is divided into 100 new-minutes, and each new-minute is divided into 100 new-seconds. The ratio of a new-second to an ordinary second is

(A) $\frac{125}{108}$ (B) $\frac{108}{125}$ (C) $\frac{144}{10\,000}$ (D) $\frac{625}{36}$ (E) $\frac{36}{625}$

1989-G7-11

9. Some of the squares in the rectangle are shaded. More squares need to be shaded so that the number of shaded squares is half the number of unshaded squares. The number of additional squares which need to be shaded are

(A) 12   (B) 8   (C) 7
(D) 5   (E) 3

1983-P-7

10. Points A, B, C, and D are placed in that order on a line so that $AB = 2BC = CD$. Then BD as a fraction of AD is

(A) $\frac{1}{2}$ (B) $\frac{3}{4}$ (C) $\frac{2}{5}$ (D) $\frac{1}{5}$ (E) none of these

1977-G-20

11. A tree of height 45 m casts a shadow of 30 m. Then the height, in metres, of a tree casting a 28 m shadow is

(A) 42   (B) $48\frac{3}{14}$ (C) $18\frac{2}{3}$ (D) 43   (E) 52

1985-G7-14

12. The midpoints of the sides of a square are joined as shown. A fraction of the original square is shaded. The fraction is

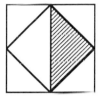

(A) $\frac{1}{2}$ (B) $\frac{1}{3}$ (C) $\frac{1}{4}$

(D) $\frac{1}{6}$ (E) $\frac{1}{8}$

1968-J-6

13. If the radius of a circle is increased by one unit, the ratio of the new circumference to the new diameter is

(A) $(\pi + 2) : 1$ (B) $(2\pi + 1) : \pi$ (C) $\pi : 1$ (D) $(2\pi - 1) : 2$ (E) $(\pi - 2) : 1$

1972-J-25

14. A cask is filled with 45 gallons of wine. Nine gallons are removed, and the cask is refilled with water. Then nine gallons of the mixture are removed and the cask is refilled with water again. The ratio of water to wine in the final mixture is

(A) $6 : 25$ (B) $9 : 16$ (C) $2 : 3$ (D) $2 : 5$ (E) none of these

1985-C-20

15. In the diagram, the curved lines are semicircles. All areas marked A are equal to one another and all areas marked B are equal to one another. The ratio of each area A to each area B is

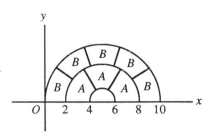

(A) $\frac{5}{6}$ (B) $\frac{3}{5}$ (C) $\frac{2}{3}$

(D) $\frac{35}{27}$ (E) none of these

Full Solution Questions

1982-P-9

1. In a class of 30 students, the ratio of boys to girls is 2 : 3. If 6 girls join the class, find the ratio of girls to boys in the class.

1976-G-6

2. Frank has $1.83 and gives Mary 25 cents. Janet has $4.99 and also gives Mary 25 cents. Find the ratio of the amount of money Frank has left to the amount of money Janet has left.

1987-G7-11

3. Two positive integers are in the ratio 2 : 5. If the product of the two integers is 40, find the larger integer.

1985-G8-22

4. Jacques is given two pieces of string, each 12 cm long. With one piece he forms a rectangle whose length is double its width. With the other piece he forms a square. Find the ratio of the area of the square to the area of the rectangle.

1982-G-26

5. The scale of a map reads 1 : 250 000. Find the distance, in km, between two towns which are 3.5 cm apart on the map.

1981-G-13

6. Three numbers are in the ratio 2 : 5 : 3. If the largest number is 60, find the other two numbers.

1982-G-12

7. In hockey standings, a win counts 2 points, a tie counts 1 point, and a loss counts 0 points. After 10 games, the Montreal Canadiens had won 5, tied 4, and lost 1. If they continued to win, lose, and tie in this ratio, determine their point total after 80 games.

1984-G-14

8. In making lawn fertilizer, a manufacturer blends nitrogen, phosphoric acid, and potash in the ratio of 3 : 8 : 17 respectively. If 6 kg of nitrogen are used in this mixture, find the amount of potash used.

1975-G-14

9. The sides of a right-angled triangle are 5 cm, 12 cm, and 13 cm. A rectangle has sides 8 cm and 10 cm. Find the ratio of the area of the triangle to the area of the rectangle.

1974-G-18

10. A man who is 6 feet tall casts a $2\frac{1}{2}$ foot shadow. If, at the same time, a telephone pole casts a 10 foot shadow, find the height of the pole.

1980-G-16

11. A sphere of radius r has surface area $4\pi r^2$ and volume $\frac{4}{3}\pi r^3$. Find the ratio of the surface area to the volume.

1990-G8-16

12. Square *PQRS* is drawn inside square *ABCD* as shown. Find the ratio of the area of *PQRS* to the area of *ABCD*.

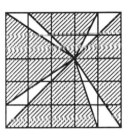

1988-G8-23

13. In the diagram drawn on the square grid, find the ratio of the shaded area to the unshaded area.

1967-J-21

14. If $a : b = 3 : 4$ and $a : (b + c) = 2 : 5$, find the value of $a : c$.

1966-J-12

15. *A*, *B*, *C*, and *D* are four points on a line such that $AB : AC = 3 : 5$ and $BD : CD = 7 : 2$. If *CD* is 5 cm long, find the length of *AB*.

Find the circumference, in metres, of a circular race track having radius 50 metres.

Circles

Multiple Choice Questions

1985-G-4

1. The chart at the right represents the number of games won, lost, and tied by the Wildcats. They played a total of 40 games. The total number they either won or tied was

   (A) 0   (B) 10   (C) 20

   (D) 30   (E) 40

Wildcat Games

1979-G-7
2. The radius of a circle having circumference 6π units is

(A) 3   (B) 4π (C) $\frac{3}{\pi}$ (D) 3π (E) 4

1971-J-4
3. The area of a circle whose radius is $\frac{1}{\pi}$ is

(A) π (B) 1   (C) $\frac{1}{\pi}$ (D) 2   (E) none of these

1968-J-12
4. The arc lengths of three semicircles are as shown. The area of the shaded region is

(A) 18π (B) 54π (C) 36π

(D) 72π (E) 144π

1977-G-17
5. A piece of string, 40 cm long, is formed into a circle with the ends of the string touching each other. The radius of the circle, in cm, is

(A) 40π (B) 80π (C) $\frac{20}{\pi}$ (D) $\frac{40}{\pi}$ (E) $\sqrt{\frac{80}{\pi}}$

1964-J-3
6. If the radius of a circle is increased by 100%, then the area is increased by

(A) 100%   (B) 200%   (C) 300%   (D) 400%   (E) none of these

1970-J-17
7. A square and a circle have equal perimeters. The ratio of the area of the square to the area of the circle is

(A) 1 : 1   (B) π : 1   (C) π : 2   (D) π : 4   (E) 1 : 4

1988-G8-20
8. The area of the square $OABC$ is 16 square units. The area of the circle with centre O and radius OA, in square units, is

(A) 8π (B) 16π (C) 4π

(D) 16   (E) 64π

1975-G-21

9. The difference between the radii of two circles is 10 cm. The difference, in cm, between their circumferences is

   (A) 10   (B) 20   (C) 20π (D) 10π (E) 100

1989-G7-23

10. In the diagram, the five circles have the same radii and touch as shown. The small square joins the centres of the four outer circles. The ratio of the area of the shaded parts of all five circles to the area of the unshaded parts of all five circles is

   (A) 1 : 3   (B) 1 : 4   (C) 2 : 5

   (D) 2 : 3   (E) 5 : 4

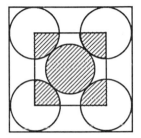

1974-G-22

11. In the diagram, *ABCD* is a square. If diagonal *AC* = 2 cm, then the area of the shaded part, in square centimetres, is

   (A) $\pi - 1$ (B) $\pi - \sqrt{2}$ (C) $\pi - 2$

   (D) $\pi + \sqrt{2}$ (E) $\pi - 4$

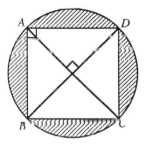

1982-G-23

12. A square is inscribed in a circle. If the area of the square is 49 cm^2, the radius of the circle, in cm, is

   (A) greater than 7   (B) equal to 7

   (C) less than $\frac{7}{2}$ (D) greater than $\frac{7}{2}$

   (E) equal to $\frac{7}{2}$

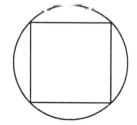

Full Solution Questions

1978-G-9

1. Find the circumference, in metres, of a circular race track having radius 50 m.

1974-G-14

2. A circle has a radius of 1 unit. Find the area of the circle in square units.

1985-G-7

3. Find the radius, in centimetres, of the largest circle which fits inside a square with a side of 10 cm.

1980-G-10

4. The area of a given circle is 9π cm². Find the diameter of this circle, in cm.

1972-J-7

5. A window consists of a rectangle surmounted by a semicircle. The rectangular portion has a width of 2 feet and a height of 3 feet. Find the perimeter of the window.

1989-G8-12

6. In the diagram, four circles with the same radii are touching as shown. The centres are connected. Find the ratio of the area of the shaded parts of the circles to the area of the unshaded parts of the circles.

1984-G-18

7. In the diagram, the circle with radius 5 units touches the insides of the square. Find the ratio of the area of the square to the area of the circle.

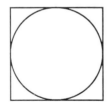

1983-P-18

8. The circle in the diagram has centre A and radius 1. If $ABCD$ is a square, find the area of the shaded region.

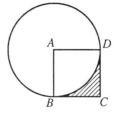

1978-J-13

9. AE is divided into four equal parts and semicircles are drawn on AC, CE, AD, and DE, creating paths from A to E as shown. Determine the ratio of the length of the upper path to the length of the lower path.

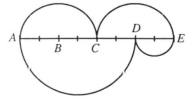

1980-J-16

10. *AB* is the diameter of the semicircle shown. If *AC* = 8, *CB* = 6, and ∠*ACB* = 90°, find the area of the shaded region.

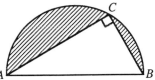

1987-G8-18

11. Sam's bicycle has wheels each of which has a diameter of 60 cm. When Sam goes for a 2 km ride on his bike, find the approximate number of times each wheel will rotate.

1984-G-23

12. In the diagram, *ABCD* is a rectangle in which *AB* = 8 cm and *BC* = 6 cm. Find the area of the circle, in cm².

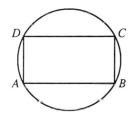

Sir Lance needs a lot of ladder to reach the top of a castle wall. At the base of the wall is a moat 5 m wide filled with crocodiles. If his 13 m ladder just reaches the top of the wall from the edge of the moat, find the height of the wall.

2-Dimensional Geometry - I

Multiple Choice Questions

1981-G-9

1. In $\triangle ABC$, $AB = AC$ and $\angle A = 50°$. The value of $\angle B$ is

   (A) 50°   (B) 60°   (C) 180°   (D) 65°   (E) 130°

1984-G-3

2. In the diagram, three straight lines intersect at one point to give six angles expressed in degrees. The value of c is

   (A) 40   (B) 60   (C) 80

   (D) 120   (E) 140

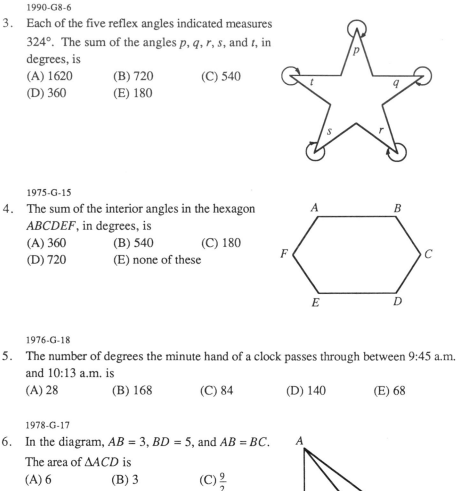

1990-G8-6

3. Each of the five reflex angles indicated measures
    324°. The sum of the angles p, q, r, s, and t, in
    degrees, is
    (A) 1620   (B) 720   (C) 540
    (D) 360   (E) 180

1975-G-15

4. The sum of the interior angles in the hexagon
    ABCDEF, in degrees, is
    (A) 360   (B) 540   (C) 180
    (D) 720   (E) none of these

1976-G-18

5. The number of degrees the minute hand of a clock passes through between 9:45 a.m.
    and 10:13 a.m. is
    (A) 28   (B) 168   (C) 84   (D) 140   (E) 68

1978-G-17

6. In the diagram, $AB = 3$, $BD = 5$, and $AB = BC$.
    The area of $\triangle ACD$ is
    (A) 6   (B) 3   (C) $\frac{9}{2}$
    (D) 8   (E) none of these

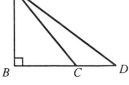

1985-G8-18

7. Sharon put four thumbtacks at P, Q, R,
    and S and she wrapped an elastic band
    around them, as in the diagram. The length
    of PS, in cm, is
    (A) 125   (B) 21   (C) 15
    (D) 10   (E) 5

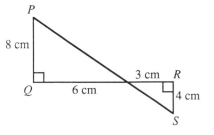

1988-G8-6

8. A ladder 5 m long is leaning against a wall 12 m high. The foot of the ladder is 3 m from the base of the wall. The distance, in metres, from the top of the ladder to the top of the wall is

(A) 4   (B) 7   (C) 8   (D) 9   (E) 10

1988-G7-17

9. Each of the equal sides of an isosceles triangle is 5 cm longer than the third side. The perimeter of the triangle is 31 cm. The length of each equal side, in centimetres, is

(A) 7   (B) 12   (C) 13   (D) 21   (E) 26

1988-G7-18

10. A square piece of paper is folded in half to form a rectangle. This rectangle has a perimeter of 18 cm. The area of the original square, in cm^2, was

(A) 9   (B) 12   (C) 18   (D) 24   (E) 36

1989-G8-5

11. The pattern in the diagram is reflected in the horizontal line. The diagram showing the correct position of the image is

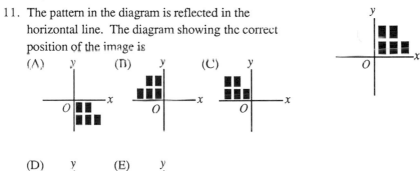

(A)   (B)   (C)

(D)   (E)

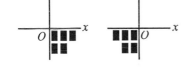

1978-G-16

12. A square room having each side of length 10 m is to have the floor covered with tiles. Each tile has dimensions 50 cm by 50 cm. The number of tiles needed to cover the floor is

(A) 400   (B) 40   (C) 500   (D) 25   (E) 4

1986-G7-24

13. The diagram on the right shows a triangle in which
    two lines are drawn to the opposite sides from each
    of two vertices. This divides the triangle into nine
    non-overlapping sections. If eight lines are drawn
    to the opposite sides, four from A and four from
    B, the number of non-overlapping sections into
    which the triangle is divided is

    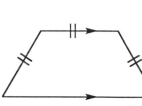

    (A) 16   (B) 25   (C) 36
    (D) 42   (E) 49

1986-P-21

14. A trapezoid has three equal sides and the base is two
    units less than the sum of these three sides. If the
    distance between the parallel sides is 5 units, then
    the area of the trapezoid, in square units, is

    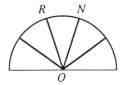

    (A) 13   (B) 35   (C) 65
    (D) 125   (E) 185

Full Solution Questions

1990-G7-2

1. A semicircular window has five identical panes
   formed by radii as illustrated in the diagram. Find
   the measure of $\angle RON$.

1982-G-7

2. In $\triangle ABC$, BC is extended to D. If $AB = AC$
   and exterior angle ACD equals $130°$, find the
   measure of angle A.

   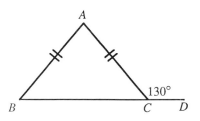

1983-G-10

3. In the diagram, find the sum of the acute angles at
   A, B, C, D, E, and F.

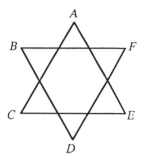

1979-G-15

4. In $\triangle ABC$, angle B is 36 degrees larger than angle A and angle C is six times angle
   A. Find the number of degrees in angle A.

1987-G7-9

5. Find the sum of all the interior angles of the
   pentagon in the diagram.

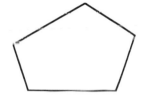

1979-G-18

6. In the diagram, $AD = 5$, $BD = 4$, and the area of
   $\triangle ACD$ is 15. Find the area of $\triangle ABC$.

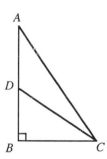

1981-G-11

7. Sir Lance needs a lot of ladder to reach the top of a castle wall. At the base of the wall
   is a moat 5 metres wide filled with crocodiles. If his 13 m ladder just reaches the top
   of the wall from the edge of the moat, find the height of the wall.

1982-G-21

8. Two vertical poles, 10 metres high and 15 metres high, stand 12 metres apart. Find
   the distance between the tops of the poles.

1987-G8-14

9. The diagram represents a regular hexagon with a perimeter of 42 cm. Find the length of the line segment *NR*.

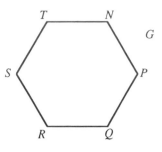

1989-G7-21

10. Four strips of wood each 30 cm long and 3 cm wide are arranged to form a square as shown. Find the area of the inner square.

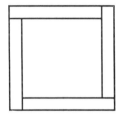

1985-G7-24

11. Michelle has a building set which includes 60 short pieces, 60 long pieces, and 60 bolts with nuts. Find the number of objects she can make, each identical to the one shown.

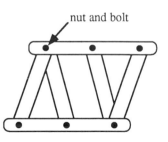

nut and bolt

1990-G7-20

12. A string, 13 cm long, is tied to form a loop. A total of 2 cm of string is used to tie the ends together. The loop is placed around three pegs to form a triangle with all sides having integer lengths in centimetres. Find the length of the longest possible side of the triangle.

1990-G8-18

13. Each side of the cross in the diagram is 1 cm. The cross is cut into pieces, all of which are rearranged to form a square. Find the length of each side of the square.

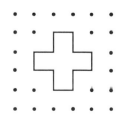

1982-G-16

14. If we wish to tile a 15 m by 8 m rectangular floor using 25 cm by 25 cm square tiles, find how many tiles we will need.

A ball which bounces straight up and down, falls from a height of 16 m. Each time, it bounces up to half the height from which it just fell. When the top of its bounce is 1 m from the ground, find the total distance it has travelled.

Number Patterns and Sequences - I

Multiple Choice Questions

1978-G-14

1. The digits of the number 9145 are arranged in descending order and then in ascending order. The difference between the resulting numbers is

(A) 3726   (B) 8192   (C) 8182   (D) 8082   (E) 4726

1988-G7-10

2. The sum of the first six multiples of 8, starting with 8, is

(A) 158   (B) 160   (C) 168   (D) 200   (E) 216

1983-G-19

3. The time is now 10:00 a.m. In 12 291 hours the time will be

(A) 12:00 p.m.   (B) 1:00 p.m.   (C) 3:00 p.m.   (D) 7:00 a.m.   (E) 9:00 a.m.

1983-G-21

4. Starting at 777 and counting backwards by 7s, a student counts 777, 770, 763, etc. A number that will be counted is

(A) 45   (B) 44   (C) 43   (D) 42   (E) 41

1986-G7-11

5. The numbers in the sequence 2, 7, 12, 17, 22, ... increase by fives. The numbers in the sequence 3, 10, 17, 24, 31, ... increase by sevens. The number 17 occurs in *both* sequences. The next number which occurs in *both* sequences is

(A) 37   (B) 52   (C) 72   (D) 87   (E) 122

1987-G8-11

6. The value of $\dfrac{190 + 192 + 194 + 196 + 198 - 200 - 202 - 204 - 206 - 208}{10}$ is

(A) −10   (B) −5   (C) 0   (D) 5   (E) 10

1986-G8-16

7. The value of $1 - 2 + 3 - 4 + 5 - 6 + ... - 100$ is

(A) −50   (B) −49   (C) 0   (D) −100   (E) −150

1985-G8-12

8. Triangular numbers follow this pattern:

1   3   6   10

As shown, the first four triangular numbers are 1, 3, 6, and 10. The seventh triangular number is

(A) 36   (B) 28   (C) 25   (D) 21   (E) 15

1989-G7-22

9. A large sheet of paper is 0.01 mm thick. It is cut in half and one piece is placed on the other to make a pile. These are cut in half and all four pieces are placed in a pile. These four are cut in half and placed in a pile, and the process is continued. After the pieces have been cut and piled for the tenth time, the height of the pile, in cm, is

(A) 0.01024   (B) 0.1024   (C) 1.024   (D) 10.24   (E) 102.4

1983-G-26

10. Observe that $1^3 + 2^3 = (1 + 2)^2$, $1^3 + 2^3 + 3^3 = (1 + 2 + 3)^2$, and $1^3 + 2^3 + 3^3 + 4^3 = (1 + 2 + 3 + 4)^2$. If the same pattern always holds, the value of $\sqrt{1^3 + 2^3 + 3^3 + 4^3 + 5^3 + 6^3 + 7^3 + 8^3 + 9^3 + 10^3}$ is

(A) $\sqrt{1000}$ (B) 3025   (C) 55   (D) $\sqrt{166375}$ (E) $\sqrt{55^3}$

1979-G-25

11. The numbers 1, 2, 3, and 4 are placed in the empty squares so that each row, each column, and each diagonal contains each of the four numbers. The sum of the numbers in the two squares marked with an asterisk (*) is:

(A) 3   (B) 4   (C) 5

(D) 6   (E) 7

1985-G7-10

12. If the pattern at the right is continued, the number of letters in the "K" column will be

(A) 10   (B) 11   (C) 19

(D) 21   (E) 23

1990-G8-21

13. The integers greater than 1 are arranged in columns P, Q, R, S, and T as shown. The column in which the integer 1000 will be found is

(A) P (B) Q (C) R

(D) S (E) T

P	Q	R	S	T
		2	3	4
7	6	5		
		8	9	10
13	12	11		
		14	15	16
19	18	17		

Full Solution Questions

1987-G7-12

1. The sum of the whole numbers from 1 to 10 inclusive is 55. Use this result to find the value of $3 + 6 + 9 + 12 + 15 + 18 + 21 + 24 + 27 + 30$.

1977-G-14

2. If the number pattern shown is continued, find the second number in the fifteenth row.

1986-G7-21

3. In the magic square on the right, the sum of the numbers in any row, column, or diagonal must be the same. Find the value of N.

10		
9		13
14	N	

1983-G-16

4. Five yeast cells were placed in a laboratory dish at 4 p.m. The number of yeast cells doubles in every 10 minute interval. Find the number of cells in the dish at the end of one hour.

1987-G7-21

5. A ball which bounces straight up and down, falls from a height of 16 m. Each time, it bounces up to half the height from which it just fell. When the top of its bounce is 1 m from the floor, find the total distance it has travelled.

1988-G8-14

6. Find the number of integers between 500 and 700 in which the sum of the digits is 12.

1985-C-11

7. The integers greater than 1 are arranged, four in each row, in five columns as follows:

a	b	c	d	e
2	3	4	5	
	9	8	7	6
10	11	12	13	
	17	16	15	14

If the pattern is followed, in which column will the number 1001 occur?

1990-G7-17

8. Each number in a sequence is obtained by adding the two previous numbers. The 6th, 7th, and 8th numbers of the sequence are 29, 47, and 76. Find the third number in the sequence.

1988-G7-8

9. While waiting for the school bus, Sally plays a counting game. After taking two steps forward, she must take one step backward. She wishes to reach a tree which is seven steps away from her. Using this rule, what is the least number of steps she must take to reach the tree?

1988-G7 21

10. The digits used to number all the pages of a book were counted. If the number of digits used was 216, find the number of pages in the book.

1990-G8-19

11. Martina was writing the numbers from 1 to 999 in order but she was interrupted part way through the count. At that point she had written a total of 288 digits. What was the last number she had written?

1985 P-21

12. What is the least number of consecutive positive integers that add up to 1000? What are these integers?

1968-J-25

13. The positive integers are arranged in the pattern indicated in the diagram. What number will be found in the square for the 61st (horizontal) row and 23rd (vertical) column?

1				
2	3			
4	5	6		
7	8	9	10	
11	12	13	14	15

In your bureau drawer there are 10 blue socks and 16 grey socks. You reach into the drawer In the dark, and pull out socks. What Is the smallest number of socks you must take to ensure that you have a matching pair?

Counting and Logic - I

Multiple Choice Questions

1976-G-2

1. Of the following statements, the one which is false is

(A) $3 > 2$ (B) $-3 < -2$ (C) $2 > -3$ (D) $-2 < -3$ (E) $5 \neq 4$

1990-G7-6

2. If K is a point $\frac{2}{3}$ of the way from J to L on the number line shown, the number located at K is

(A) 50   (B) 56   (C) 62

(D) 68   (E) 80

1974-G-13

3. In your bureau drawer there are 10 blue socks and 16 grey socks. You reach into the drawer in the dark, and pull out socks. The smallest number of socks you must take to ensure that you have a matching pair is

(A) 2   (B) 3   (C) 11   (D) 26   (E) 6

1985-G7-15

4. Jane was born on June 30, 1974. Alex was born on June 3, 1975. The number of days between their birthdates (not including their birthdates) is

(A) 337   (B) 338   (C) 339   (D) 393   (E) 394

1987-G7-15

5. Triominoes are made of three squares and come in two shapes, ⬜⬜⬜ and ⬜⬜ shape

If you had a box of triominoes, with several of each shape, the pattern below which could be made using only triominoes is

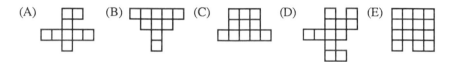

(A)   (B)   (C)   (D)   (E)

1981-G-16

6. At the end of the season, the standings of the teams in a school soccer league were

Team	Games Played	Wins	Losses	Ties	Goals For	Goals Against	Points
Drillers	12	8	3		60	36	
Blizzard	12	7	3		51	41	
Kickers	12	4	4		48	48	
Flames	12	3	7		39	50	
White Caps	12	3	8		37	60	

Each win earns two points and a tie earns one point. The points earned by these teams, in order of standing, were

(A) 17, 16, 14, 12, 8   (B) 17, 16, 12, 8, 7

(C) 17, 14, 12, 10, 7   (D) 8, 7, 4, 3, 3

(E) 24, 18, 12, 8, 7

1984-G-17

7. In the product shown at the right, the letters P and Q represent different digits from 1 to 9. Then P and Q, in order, are

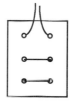

$$\begin{array}{r} P\,8 \\ 3\,Q \\ \hline 2730 \end{array}$$

  (A) 3, 5   (B) 7, 4   (C) 9, 4

  (D) 9, 5   (E) 7, 5

1988-G7-20

8. January 1, 1986 occurred on a Wednesday. January 1, 1992 will occur on a

  (A) Tuesday   (B) Wednesday (C) Thursday   (D) Friday   (E) Saturday

1989 G7-19

9. A single piece of string is laced through holes in a piece of cardboard. The top side of the card is shown. Of the diagrams below, the one that could not be the underside of the card is

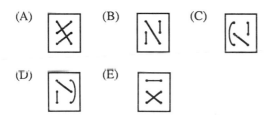

(A)   (B)   (C)

(D)   (E)

1989-G7-24

10. After a successful game of marbles with three friends, Jason said, "If only I had one more marble, I would have four times as many as Marie, five times as many as Jennifer, and seven times as many as Tony". The least number of marbles Jason could have had was

  (A) 34   (B) 35   (C) 139   (D) 140   (E) 141

1978-G-24

11. Two couples share a park bench. Neither couple wishes to be separated. The number of different seating arrangements, from a position in front of the bench, which allows the couples to stay together is

  (A) 1   (B) 2   (C) 3   (D) 4   (E) 8

1984-G-24

12. The total number of squares included in the diagram
    is
    (A) 24   (B) 39   (C) 47
    (D) 49   (E) 50

1986-G7-25

13. There are five short pieces of chain, each with three
    links. If it costs 10¢ to cut a link and 25¢ to weld it
    back together, the lowest cost, in dollars, to make
    the longest possible chain is
    (A) 0.70   (B) 0.95   (C) 1.05
    (D) 1.40   (E) 1.95

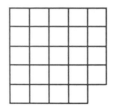

1987-G8-24

14. Cecile and Tanya together have $4.50. Cecile has only quarters while Tanya has only
    dimes. One of them has four more coins than the other. The number of coins
    possessed by the two of them together is
    (A) 20   (B) 24   (C) 27   (D) 30   (E) 36

Full Solution Questions

1990-G8-3

1. An odd number between 301 and 370 has three different digits. If the sum of its digits
   is five times the hundreds digit, find the number.

1985-G7-9

2. The digits of the number 4795 can be rearranged to form different numbers. What is
   the sum of the largest and the smallest numbers that may be formed?

1990-G7-9

3. What is the number of hours and minutes from 6:14 a.m. sunrise until 8:02 p.m.
   sunset?

1977-G-10

4. What is the maximum number of points of intersection of four distinct straight lines?

1980-G-12

5. What is the number of ways that a sum of seven can occur when two ordinary dice, one black and one white, are rolled?

1980-G-13

6. Two logs found in a wood pile are identical in every respect. Using a power saw it takes nine seconds to cut the first log into four smaller logs. What is the time required to cut the second log into five smaller logs?

1986-G7-14

7. The number 1 is both the square of an integer and the cube of an integer. What is the next larger integer which is both a square and a cube of a positive integer?

1988-G7-15

8. A calendar watch loses one second per day.
At this rate, what is the approximate length of time, in years, for the watch to lose exactly 24 hours?

1984-G-15

9. In the diagram, the sum of each line of four numbers is 24. Find the value of y.

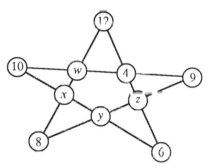

1990-G7-15

10. Mr. Johnson packaged 126 kg of potatoes to sell at the market. He put the potatoes into 2 kg and 5 kg bags. If he used the same number of bags of each type, find the total number of bags used.

1990-G7-16

11. One mouse said to another, "If you give me one piece of cheese, then we will have an equal number of pieces". The other mouse replied, "If you give me one piece, then I will have double the number you have". What is the total number of pieces that the mice have?

1974-G-17

12. Nine coins are used to make a value of $1.35. If the coins are quarters or dimes, what is the number of dimes used?

1976-G-20

13. The diameter of a coin is $\frac{3}{4}$ inches. Coins are placed on a rectangular sheet measuring 6 inches by 12 inches. If no coins overlap or overhang the edge of the sheet, what is the largest number of coins that may be arranged on the sheet?

1976-G-24

14. There are six persons in a room. Each person shakes hands with each of the other persons in the room. What is the total number of mutual handshakes?

1986-G7-23

15. Of the 33 students in a class, 18 belong to the mathematics club, 17 belong to the science club, and 4 belong to neither club. What is the number of students who belong to both clubs?

1990-G8-20

16. For their project, some students needed thirty poles, each 6 units long, twenty poles, each 8 units long, and ten poles, each 10 units long. The poles were only available in 16 unit lengths. Assuming no gluing and no loss in cutting, what is the least number of 16 unit length poles needed?

An ant wishes to travel from *A* to *B* on the surface of a wooden block with dimensions $2 \times 4 \times 8$ as shown. What is the shortest distance it can walk?

3-Dimensional Geometry - I

Multiple Choice Questions

1988-G7-5

1. The number of pairs of parallel faces on a cube is
   (A) 4   (B) 3   (C) 2   (D) 1   (E) 0

1974-G-20

2. If a rectangular block has a length of 12 mm, a width of 10 mm, and a depth of 8 mm, its volume in cubic centimetres is
   (A) 960   (B) 0.096   (C) 0.96   (D) 96   (E) 9600

1983-G-18

3. If the volume of a cube is 64 cm^3, then the total surface area, in cm^2, is
   (A) 16   (B) 64   (C) 96   (D) 256   (E) 384

1985-G7-19

4. The sides of a cube are doubled in length to form a larger cube. The number of original small cubes required to fill the larger cube is

(A) 2   (B) 4   (C) 6   (D) 8   (E) 16

1989-G7-13

5. A box has four flaps labelled $P, Q, R,$ and S.
   Without moving the box, the flaps are folded over in
   the order R, S, Q, P. For a person standing at
   point X and looking down on the box from the top,
   the appearance of the box is

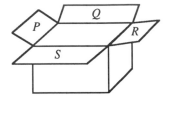

(A) 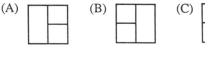   (B)   (C)

X

(D)   (E)

1990-G7-14

6. It takes a backhoe one hour to dig a 3 m by 3 m by 3 m hole. The number of hours needed for two backhoes, each working at the same rate, to dig a 6 m by 6 m by 6 m hole, is

(A) 1   (B) 2   (C) 4   (D) 8   (E) 16

1973-J-8

7. A rectangular $4 \times 3 \times 2$ block has its surface painted red, and then is cut into cubes with each edge 1 unit. The number of cubes having exactly one of its faces painted red is

(A) 0   (B) 4   (C) 8   (D) 12   (E) 24

1987-G7-17

8. The figure shown is made up of 27 identical cubes.
   The cube marked K is removed. The effect that
   this has on the total surface area of the figure is to

(A) increase it by 2 cm²   (B) increase it by 1 cm²

(C) leave it unchanged   (D) decrease it by 1 cm²

(E) decrease it by 2 cm²

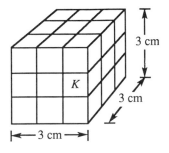

3 cm

3 cm

3 cm

1987-G8-20

9. The volume of a cylinder is equal to the area of the base times the height of the cylinder. The volume, in cm³, of the largest cylinder which will fit inside a cube 10 cm by 10 cm by 10 cm is

(A) 25π (B) 100π (C) 250π (D) 500π (E) 1000π

1967-J-24

10. An ant wishes to travel from A to B on the surface of a wooden block with dimensions $2 \times 4 \times 8$ as shown. The shortest distance it can walk is

(A) 14   (B) $2 + \sqrt{80}$ (C) $8 + \sqrt{20}$

(D) $4 + \sqrt{68}$ (E) 10

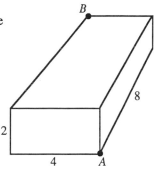

1990-G7-25

11. A 5 by 5 by 5 cube is formed using 1 by 1 by 1 cubes. A number of the smaller cubes are removed by punching out the 15 designated columns from front to back, top to bottom, and side to side. The number of smaller cubes remaining is

(A) 50   (B) 52   (C) 60

(D) 68   (E) 72

1969-J-17

12. A rectangular box has dimensions r, s, and t units, where $r < s < t$. If one dimension only is increased by one, then the increase in volume

(A) is greatest when r is increased

(B) is greatest when s is increased

(C) is greatest when t is increased

(D) is the same regardless of which dimension is increased

(E) cannot be determined from the information given

Full Solution Questions

1984-G-7

1. How many edges are there on a triangular-based prism?

1989-G7-17

2. A parcel is tied with ribbon as shown. The bow requires 47 cm of ribbon. What is the total length of the ribbon?

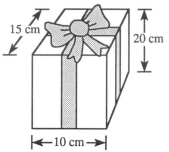

15 cm

20 cm

|←10 cm→|

1978-G-22

3. A rectangular box has volume 15 cm³. If the length, width, and height are doubled, what is the volume of the resulting box?

1979-G-23

4. A 3 × 3 × 3 cube is painted red and then cut into 27 unit cubes. How many of these small cubes will have paint on exactly two faces?

1987-G7-20

5. A square piece of cardboard has an area of 36 cm². A square of 1 cm² is cut from each corner. The sides are folded in order to make an open box. What is the volume of this box?

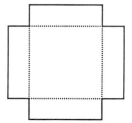

1987-P-25

6. The surface of a cube is to be painted so that no two faces of the same colour share a common edge. What is the minimum number of different colours required to paint the cube?

1981-G-19

7. The volume of a sphere is given by the formula $V = \frac{4}{3}\pi r^3$, where r is the radius of the sphere. What is the volume of the largest sphere which can fit entirely in a box having dimensions 6 by 6 by 6?

1966-J-18

8. A rectangular tank with base a square of side 4 feet contains water to a height of 3 feet. A solid cube of edge 2 feet is placed on the bottom of the tank. What is the new height of the water?

1988-P-21

9. An open box is constructed by gluing a number of 1 cm cubes together to form the bottom and the sides. The outside dimensions of the finished box are 10 cm by 10 cm by 10 cm, and the sides and bottom are all 1 cm thick. Determine the number of cubes required to construct the box.

1987-P-22

10. A fish tank, filled with water, is 100 cm long, 60 cm wide, and 40 cm high. It is tilted, as shown, resting on a 60 cm edge, with the water level reaching C, the midpoint of AB. Find the depth of water in the fish tank once AB is returned to a horizontal position.

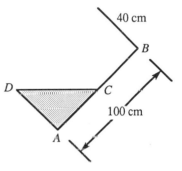

1988-G8-24

11. Each of the numbers 1, 2, 3, 4, 5, and 6 is painted, one to a face, on the faces of a cube. The cube is placed on a table so that from each of three positions a person can see the top and two of the other faces. The sums of numbers showing on the visible faces from the three positions are 9, 14, and 15. What number is on the bottom face?

1986-P-24

12. A cube having an edge length of 10 is sliced into two sections by a cut in the plane ABC, as shown in the diagram. Find the volume of the smaller section.

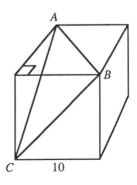

Two men and two boys wish to cross a river. Their small canoe will carry the weight of only one man or two boys. What is the minimum number of times the canoe must cross the river to get all four people on the opposite shore?

Challenge Problems

Multiple Choice Questions

1975-G-8

1. The sum of two numbers is 11 and their product is 24. The sum of their reciprocals is

   (A) $\frac{2}{11}$ (B) $\frac{11}{24}$ (C) $\frac{1}{24}$ (D) $\frac{11}{28}$ (E) $\frac{11}{30}$

1989-G8-6

2. The numbers 3 and 6 have a sum of 9 and a product of 18. The sum is a factor of the product. Another pair of numbers with this property is

   (A) 6, 12   (B) 5, 10   (C) 4, 8   (D) 2, 4   (E) 1, 2

1983-G-13

3. The points $A(3, 4)$, $B(4, 3)$, $C(-3, -4)$, $D(3, -4)$, and $E(4, -3)$ are marked on a coordinate grid. The line segment that is horizontal is

    (A) *AD*   (B) *BE*   (C) *BC*   (D) *CD*   (E) *AB*

1985-G8-13

4. The result obtained by subtracting the square of a number from the number is greatest when the number is

    (A) 5   (B) 1   (C) $\frac{1}{2}$ (D) $\frac{1}{10}$ (E) –5

1985-G8-15

5. The product of two integers is –24. A difference between the same two integers is –11. The sum of the integers could be

    (A) –14   (B) –11   (C) –10   (D) –5   (E) 11

1989-G8-20

6. A rectangle is divided into three rectangles of different areas and a square *GHFD*. The area of rectangle *AEHG* is 21 cm², and the area of rectangle *HJCF* is 28 cm². If all rectangles have lengths and widths which are integers, the area of the square *GHFD*, in cm², could be

    (A) 49   (B) 36   (C) 35

    (D) 16   (E) 9

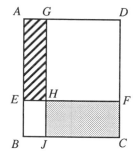

1986-G8-17

7. The sum of two integers is –4. Their product is –21. The greater integer is

    (A) –7   (B) –3   (C) –1   (D) 3   (E) 7

1989-G7-18

8. Tina bought a sweater for $13.98 and gave the cashier $20.00. By mistake, the cashier gave Tina $13.98 in change. In order to correct the error, the amount, in dollars, that Tina should return to the cashier is

    (A) 6.02   (B) 6.96   (C) 7.96   (D) 12.04   (E) 13.98

1975-G-22

9. Beginning precisely at 6 o'clock, it takes 5 seconds for a clock to strike 6 o'clock. If the strikings are uniformly spaced, the time, in seconds, to strike 12 o'clock is

    (A) $9\frac{1}{5}$ (B) 10   (C) $14\frac{2}{5}$ (D) 12   (E) 11

1988-G8-22

10. If each of m and n is a fraction between zero and one, then it is always true that

(A) $m \times n < 1$ (B) $m + n < 1$ (C) $\frac{m}{n} < 1$ (D) $m + n > 1$ (E) $m^2 + n^2 > 1$

1989-G8-23

11. One year a basketball team played 180 games. They never lost more than 3 games in a row and never won more than 5 games in a row. The number of games the team won must have been

(A) no more than 36   (B) no more than 45   (C) no more than 135

(D) no more than 150   (E) exactly 111

1987-G7-22

12. The sum of all whole numbers less than 100, which are multiples of 6 and end in a 4, is

(A) 162   (B) 108   (C) 1306   (D) 78   (E) 138

1986-G8-25

13. Two men and two boys wish to cross a river. Their small canoe will carry the weight of only one man or two boys. The minimum number of times the canoe must cross the river to get all four people on the opposite shore is

(A) 5   (B) 6   (C) 7   (D) 8   (E) 9

1974-G-25

14. A car is driven up a one-mile long hill at 30 m.p.h., and continues down the other side, which is also one mile in length. The speed the car must be driven on the down slope, in m.p.h., in order to average 60 m.p.h. for the whole trip, is

(A) 30   (B) 90   (C) 60   (D) 120   (E) none of these

1987 G8-25

15. If x, y, and z are three different positive integers and $(xy)^2 = xyz$, then a possible value for z is

(A) 1   (B) 5   (C) 9   (D) 11   (E) 16

Full Solution Questions

1981-G-10

1. Two positive integers have a sum of 7 and a product of 12. Find the sum of the squares of these two numbers.

1980-G-22

2. The town of Canton is west of Mason. Sinclair is east of Canton but west of Mason. Dexter is east of Richmond but west of Sinclair and Canton. Of the five towns listed, find the one which is farthest west.

1989-G7-16

3. A four-digit number has its hundreds and tens digits sum to two. The thousands digit is 7 times the tens digit, and the units digit is 5 more than the hundreds digit. Find the number.

1976-G-21

4. The sum of a number, its square, and its square root is 276. Find this number.

1975-G-23

5. A dog and a rabbit are 160 metres apart. The dog chases the rabbit. For every 9 metres that the dog runs, the rabbit jumps 7 metres. Find the distance, in metres, that the dog must run in order to overtake the rabbit.

1979-G-22

6. A ferry boat, when filled, can carry 6 Pintos and 7 Toyotas or 8 Pintos and 4 Toyotas. If the ferry boat carries Toyotas only, find the maximum number aboard.

1976-G-23

7. A palindrome is a number which remains the same when its digits are written in reverse order. For example, 131 is a palindrome. A car's odometer reads 15951. Find the least number of miles required for the next palindrome to appear.

1990-G7-21

8. Four cats and three kittens weigh 44 kg. Three cats and two kittens weigh 32 kg. If all cats have equal weights and all kittens have equal weights, find the weight, in kilograms, of two cats and one kitten.

1983-G-24

9. In the equation $2x + 3y = 24$, the variables x and y are positive integers or 0, i.e., 0, 1, 2, 3, ... Find the number of ordered pairs which satisfy this equation.

1981-G-24

10. Find the number of digits that are required to number the pages of a book from 1 to 250.

1989-G7-25

11. Between the digits of a two-digit square, a third digit is inserted to create a three-digit square. Find the number of three-digit squares that can be obtained by this process.

1974-G-26

12. At present, the sum of the ages of a father and his son is 33 years. Find the smallest number of years until the father's age is 4 times the son's age.

1978-G-26

13. *ABCD* is a rectangle inscribed in a quarter circle. If $AD = 12$ and $CE = 1$, find the length of AB.

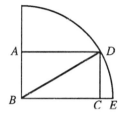

Solutions

Decimals

Multiple Choice Questions

1. Solution
    $$1 + \frac{24}{100} = 1 + 0.24$$
    $$= 1.24$$
    The answer is C.

2. Solution
    $$25 \div 0.05 = \frac{25}{0.05}$$
    $$= \frac{2500}{5}$$
    $$= 500$$
    The answer is B.

3. Solution
    $$0.2 \times 0.2 \times 0.2 = (0.2 \times 0.2) \times 0.2$$
    $$= 0.04 \times 0.2$$
    $$= 0.008$$
    The answer is D.

4. Solution
    $$2 + \frac{7}{100} + \frac{3}{1000} = 2 + 0.07 + 0.003$$
    $$= 2.073$$
    The answer is B.

5. Solution
    $$\frac{10}{0.1} - 10 = \frac{100}{1} - 10$$
    $$= 100 - 10$$
    $$= 90$$
    The answer is B.

6. Solution
    $0.435 \div 0.0821$ can be approximated by evaluating $0.4 \div 0.08$.

$$0.4 \div 0.08 = \frac{0.4}{0.08}$$
$$= \frac{40}{8}$$
$$= 5$$

The answer is D.

7. Solution

Since $\frac{60.1}{0.99}$ is approximately equal to 60 and 3.95 is approximately equal to 4,

$$\sqrt{\frac{60.1}{0.99} + 3.95} \approx \sqrt{60 + 4}$$
$$= \sqrt{64}$$
$$= 8$$

The answer is B.

8. Solution

$$(9.2 - 8.679) \times 0.003 = 0.521 \times 0.003$$
$$= 0.001563$$

The answer is E.

9. Solution

The numbers written in decreasing order of magnitude are
1.1, 1.0101, 1.01, 1.00101, 1.001.
The smallest of the numbers is 1.001.
The answer is C.

10. Solution

$$\frac{1}{2} + \frac{1}{3} = 0.5 + 0.3333...$$
$$= 0.8333...$$
$$= 0.8\overline{3}$$

The answer is D.

11. Solution

The numbers in the set written in decreasing order of magnitude are
0.9, 0.3, 0.27, 0.18, 0.081.
The second largest is 0.3.
The answer is A.

12. Solution

$$A = \frac{0.1}{0.5} = \frac{1}{5} = 0.2$$

$B = \frac{0.5}{1} = 0.5$

$C = \frac{1}{0.5} = \frac{10}{5} = 2$

Hence, $C > B > A$.

The answer is E.

13. <u>Solution</u>

$\frac{(0.3)^3}{0.9} = \frac{0.027}{0.9}$

$\qquad = \frac{0.27}{9}$

$\qquad = 0.03$

The answer is D.

14. <u>Solution</u>

$P = 0.25$

$Q = (0.25)^2 = 0.0625$

$R = \sqrt{0.25} = 0.5$

Hence, $R > P > Q$.

The answer is D.

15. <u>Solution</u>

$\left[0.1 + \frac{1}{0.1}\right]^2 = \left[0.1 + \frac{10}{1}\right]^2$

$\qquad\qquad = (10.1)^2$

$\qquad\qquad = 102.01$

The answer is C.

16. <u>Solution</u>

$0.3 = \frac{3}{10} = \frac{27}{90}$

$0.\dot{3} = \frac{1}{3} = \frac{30}{90}$

$(0.\dot{3})^2 = \left(\frac{1}{3}\right)^2 = \frac{1}{9} = \frac{10}{90}$

$\frac{1}{0.3} = \frac{10}{3} = \frac{300}{90}$

$\frac{1}{0.\dot{3}} = \frac{1}{\frac{1}{3}} = \frac{3}{1} = \frac{270}{90}$

The middle number, in magnitude, is $\frac{30}{90}$ or $0.\dot{3}$.

The answer is B.

Full Solution Questions

1. Solution
    $2.0063 + 1.532 + 0.28 = 3.8183.$

2. Solution
    $6.9 - 4.91 = 1.99.$

3. Solution
    $0.48 + 10.2 + 0.03 + 8 = 18.71.$

4. Solution
    $$0.2 \div 0.4 = \frac{0.2}{0.4}$$
    $$= \frac{2}{4}$$
    $$= 0.5$$

5. Solution
    $$0.1 \div 0.02 = \frac{0.1}{0.02}$$
    $$= \frac{10}{2}$$
    $$= 5$$

6. Solution
    $$23.1 \div 0.11 = \frac{23.1}{0.11}$$
    $$= \frac{2310}{11}$$
    $$= 210$$

7. Solution
    $$\frac{0.01}{0.002} = \frac{10}{2}$$
    $$= 5$$

8. Solution
    $$(14.2 - 1.69) \div 0.03 = \frac{12.51}{0.03}$$
    $$= \frac{1251}{3}$$
    $$= 417$$

9. Solution

$\frac{1}{7} = 0.142857142857... = 0.\dot{1}4285\dot{7}.$

10. Solution

$(0.1)^2 - (0.1)^3 = 0.01 - 0.001$
$= 0.009$

11. Solution

$\frac{a}{b} \times \frac{b}{a} - a = \frac{ab}{ba} - a$
$= 1 - a$

If $a = 1.14$, $1 - a = 1 - 1.41$
$= -0.41$

12. Solution

His cost per balloon is 12 cents and his selling price is 20 cents, so he makes 8 cents profit per balloon.

His profit for the day is $20 \times 12 \times 8 = 1920$ cents or \$19.20.

13. Solution

Since $x = 0.3$, $\frac{1}{x} = \frac{1}{0.3}$
$= \frac{10}{3}$
$= 3.\dot{3}$

14. Solution

The length of the strip is $2(3.35) + 3(2.25) = 13.45$ cm.

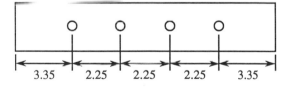

15. Solution 1

The car from company *A* costs \$3.00 less per day in fixed charge, but 1 cent more for each kilometre driven than the corresponding costs for the car from company *B*. Hence, the car from company *A* costs $2(-3) + 1550(0.01) = 15.50 - 6 = \$9.50$ more than the cost of the car from company *B*.

Solution 2

The total cost of a car from company A is $2(11) + 1550(0.05) = \$99.50$.

The total cost of a car from company B is $2(14) + 1550(0.04) = \$90.00$.

Therefore the difference between the two companies is $\$99.50 - \$90.00 = \$9.50$.

16. Solution

The first link contributes 2 cm to the total length.

The second link, and each succeeding link, contributes only 1.5 cm to the total length $(2.00 - 2 \times 0.25)$.

The total length of a 100 link chain is $2 + 99(1.5) = 150.5$ cm.

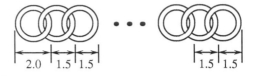

Operations with Integers - I

Multiple Choice Questions

1. Solution

$11 - 3(5 - 2)$
$= 11 - 3(3)$
$= 11 - 9$
$= 2$
The answer is B.

2. Solution

$\left(6 + 5 \times 4^2\right) \div 2$
$= \left(6 + 5 \times 16\right) \div 2$
$= \left[6 + \left(5 \times 16\right)\right] \div 2$
$= (6 + 80) \div 2$
$= 86 \div 2$
$= 43$
The answer is E.

3. Solution

$12 + 6 \div 3 \times 2 - 1$
$= 12 + (6 \div 3) \times 2 - 1$
$= 12 + 2 \times 2 - 1$
$= 12 + \left(2 \times 2\right) - 1$
$= 12 + 4 - 1$
$= (12 + 4) - 1$
$= 16 - 1$
$= 15$
The answer is A.

4. Solution

In a flowchart the operations must be done as ordered.
Hence the flowchart is equivalent to
$(13 + 7) \div 5 - 1$
$= 20 \div 5 - 1$
$= 4 - 1$
$= 3$
The answer is A.

5. Solution

    $16 - 9 = 7$

    $(3 - 4)(3 + 4) = (-1)(7) = -7$

    $(4 + 3)(4 - 3) = (7)(1) = 7$

    $-4 + 11 = 7$

    $\sqrt{49} = +7$

    The answer is B.

6. Solution

    $5 \times 10^5 + 5 \times 10^3 + 5 \times 10^2 + 5$

    $= 5(100000) + 5(1000) + 5(100) + 5$

    $= 500\,000 + 5000 + 500 + 5$

    $= 505\,505$

    The answer is D.

7. Solution

    Since $6 + 8 \div 2 = 6 + (8 \div 2) = 6 + 4 = 10$, the operations respectively are + and ÷.

    The answer is E.

    Since order of operations is an inherent part of computation, it is interesting to see the results of 6, 8, and 2 joined by any of the four basic operations of +, −, ×, and ÷. Since there are four operations connected with four operations, the number of possibilities is $4 \times 4 = 16$.

    In the following example the same operation may be repeated.

    The following are the results of these sixteen different combinations.

    $6 + 8 + 2 = (6 + 8) + 2 = 14 + 2 = 16$

    $6 + 8 - 2 = (6 + 8) - 2 = 14 - 2 = 12$

    $6 + 8 \times 2 = 6 + (8 \times 2) = 6 + 16 = 22$

    $6 + 8 \div 2 = 6 + (8 \div 2) = 6 + 4 = 10$

    $6 - 8 + 2 = (6 - 8) + 2 = -2 + 2 = 0$

    $6 - 8 - 2 = (6 - 8) - 2 = -2 - 2 = -4$

    $6 - 8 \times 2 = 6 - (8 \times 2) = 6 - 16 = -10$

    $6 - 8 \div 2 = 6 - (8 \div 2) = 6 - 4 = 2$

    $6 \times 8 + 2 = (6 \times 8) + 2 = 48 + 2 = 50$

    $6 \times 8 - 2 = (6 \times 8) - 2 = 48 - 2 = 46$

    $6 \times 8 \times 2 = (6 \times 8) \times 2 = 48 \times 2 = 96$

    $6 \times 8 \div 2 = (6 \times 8) \div 2 = 48 \div 2 = 24$

    $6 \div 8 + 2 = (6 \div 8) + 2 = \frac{3}{4} + 2 = 2\frac{3}{4}$

    $6 \div 8 - 2 = (6 \div 8) - 2 = \frac{3}{4} - 2 = -1\frac{1}{4}$

$6 \div 8 \times 2 = (6 \div 8) \times 2 = \frac{3}{4} \times 2 = \frac{3}{2}$

$6 \div 8 \div 2 = (6 \div 8) \div 2 = \frac{3}{4} \div 2 = \frac{3}{8}$

8. Solution
   $\sqrt{100 - 36} = \sqrt{64}$
   $= 8$
   The answer is E.

9. Solution
   If $a = 2$, then $4a^3 = 4(2)^3 = 4(8) = 32$.
   The answer is B.

10. Solution 1
    The answer after multiplying by 10 is 600.
    The display before the multiplication must have been $600 \div 10 = 60$.
    Upon dividing this answer by 10 the result is $60 \div 10 = 6$.
    Therefore the correct answer is 6.

    Solution 2
    By multiplying the display by 10 instead of dividing by 10, the answer on display is
    $10 \times 10 = 100$ times larger than the desired result.
    Therefore the correct answer is $600 \div 100 = 6$.
    The answer is B.

11. Solution
    When $x = 2$ and $y = -3$,
    $x^3 - y^3 = (2)^3 - (-3)^3$
    $= 8 - (-27)$
    $= 8 + 27$
    $= 35$
    The answer is C.

12. Solution
    When $n = 0$, $4n - 6 = 0 - 6 = -6$.
    When $n = 1$, $4n - 6 = 4 - 6 = -2$.
    When $n = 2$, $4n - 6 = 8 - 6 = 2$.
    When $n = 3$, $4n - 6 = 12 - 6 = 6$.
    The sum of these numbers is $-6 - 2 + 2 + 6 = 0$.
    The answer is A.

Full Solution Questions

1. Solution
   $6 + 5(7 - 3) \div 2$
   $= 6 + 5(4) \div 2$
   $= 6 + 20 \div 2$
   $= 6 + (20 \div 2)$
   $= 6 + 10$
   $= 16$

2. Solution
   $12 + 4(3 - 7)$
   $= 12 + 4(-4)$
   $= 12 - 16$
   $= -4$

3. Solution
   When $x = 4$, $3x^2 + 7 = 3(4)^2 + 7$
   $ = 3(16) + 7$
   $ = 48 + 7$
   $ = 55$

4. Solution
   When $a = 2$, $b = 3$, and $c = 4$, $bc^a = 3(4)^2$
   $ = 3(16)$
   $ = 48$

5. Solution
   $3 \times 10^5 + 4 \times 10^3 + 7 \times 10^2 + 5$
   $= 3(100\,000) + 4(1\,000) + 7(100) + 5$
   $= 300\,000 + 4\,000 + 700 + 5$
   $= 304\,705$

6. Solution
   $-1^2 - 1^3$
   $= -(1)(1) - (1)(1)(1)$
   $= -1 - 1$
   $= -2$

7. Solution

$3^2 + 4^3 + 2^4$
$= (3 \times 3) + (4 \times 4 \times 4) + (2 \times 2 \times 2 \times 2)$
$= 9 + 64 + 16$
$= 89$

8. Solution 1
When $a - 2$ and $b = 3$,
$(a^b)^2 = (2^3)^2 = (2 \times 2 \times 2)^2 = 8^2 = 64.$

Solution 2
When $a = 2$ and $b = 3$,
$(a^b)^2 = a^{2b} = 2^6 = 64.$

9. Solution
When $x = 2$ and $y = 3$, $-x^2 + (-y)^3 = -(2)^2 + (-3)^3$
$= -(2)(2) + (-3)(-3)(-3)$
$= -(4) + (-27)$
$= -4 - 27$
$= -31$

10. Solution
If $x = 7$, then $xy = 91$ is equivalent to $7y = 91$, so $y = 13$.
Therefore, $x + 2y = 7 + 2(13)$
$= 7 + 26$
$= 33$

11. Solution
Using the formula $a^2 - b^2 = (a + b)(a - b)$,
$2501^2 - 2500^2 = (2501 + 2500)(2501 - 2500)$
$= (5001)(1)$
$= 5001$

12. Solution
When $n = 1$, $3 + 2n = 3 + 2(1) = 3 + 2 = 5$.
When $n = 2$, $3 + 2n = 3 + 2(2) = 3 + 4 = 7$.
When $n = 3$, $3 + 2n = 3 + 2(3) = 3 + 6 = 9$.
When $n = 4$, $3 + 2n = 3 + 2(4) = 3 + 8 = 11$.
The resulting sum is $5 + 7 + 9 + 11 = 32$.

Percentages - I

Multiple Choice Questions

1. Solution

    1000% of 2 $= \frac{1000}{100} \times 2$

    $\qquad\qquad = 20$

    The answer is D.

2. Solution

    0.75% of 264 $= \frac{0.75}{100} \times 264$

    $\qquad\qquad\quad = 0.0075 \times 264$

    $\qquad\qquad\quad = 1.98$

    The answer is D.

3. Solution 1

    The total cost, including the sales tax, is 105% of $8.80 $= 1.05 \times \$8.80$

    $\qquad\qquad\qquad\qquad\qquad\qquad\qquad\qquad\qquad\qquad\quad = \$9.24.$

    Solution 2

    The sales tax is 5% of $8.80 $= 0.05 \times \$8.80$

    $\qquad\qquad\qquad\qquad\qquad\quad = \$0.44.$

    The total cost is $8.80 + $0.44 = $9.24.

    The answer is D.

4. Solution

    Her marks, in percent, on the five tests were 80, 94, 92, 80, and 85.

    The highest percent was on the test with the mark $\frac{47}{50}$.

    The answer is B.

5. Solution 1

    After the 25% discount, the price of the skis was $0.75 \times \$90.00 = \$67.50$.

    After a further 10% discount, the price of the skis was $0.90 \times \$67.50 = \$60.75$.

    Solution 2

    The final price of the skis was $0.90\left[0.75 \times \$90.00\right] = \$60.75$.

    The answer is E.

6. Solution
   The interest on the loan was $4200 − $3500 = $700.
   The annual rate of interest was $\frac{700}{3500} \times 100\% = \frac{1}{5} \times 100\%$
   $$= 20\%.$$
   The answer is C.

7. Solution 1
   The increase in price of dry cleaning a jacket is $1.00.
   This represents a price which is $\frac{500}{400} \times 100\% = 125\%$ of the original price.
   The new cost of dry cleaning a coat will be 125% of $10.00 $= \frac{125}{100} \times \$10.00$
   $$= \$12.50.$$

   Solution 2
   Let x represent the new price of dry cleaning a coat.
   Since the price of cleaning a jacket and the price of cleaning a coat rise by the same percentage increase, the ratios of the old price to the new price will be the same for both jackets and coats.
   Therefore $\frac{5.00}{4.00} = \frac{x}{10.00}$.
   Hence $x = (5.00)(10.00) \div 4.00 = 12.50$.
   Therefore the new cost of dry cleaning a coat is $12.50.
   The answer is E.

8. Solution 1
   80 American cents were equivalent to 100 Canadian cents.
   1 American cent was equivalent to $\frac{100}{80} = \frac{5}{4}$ Canadian cents.
   100 American cents were equivalent to $100 \times \frac{5}{4} = 125$ Canadian cents.
   Therefore, one American dollar was equivalent to $1.25 in Canadian currency.

   Solution 2
   Let x represent the value of $1.00 American in Canadian currency.
   Since the ratios of the value of Canadian currency to American currency remain the same, then $\frac{1.00}{0.80} = \frac{x}{1.00}$.
   Therefore $x = (1.00)(1.00) \div 0.80 = 1.25$.
   Hence one American dollar was equivalent to $1.25 in Canadian currency.
   The answer is B.

9. Solution
   Since the team plays 20 + 25 + 15 = 60 games, it must win 60% of 60
   $$= 0.6 \times 60 = 36 \text{ games.}$$

Since the team has only 15 games remaining, it is impossible for it to win the required 16 additional games to qualify for the playoffs.
The answer is E.

10. Solution
The number of people who voted was $10\,575 + 7990 + 2585 = 21\,150$.
Let the number of eligible voters be V.
Thus, 90% of $V = \frac{9}{10}V = 21\,150$
$$V = \frac{10}{9} \times 21\,150$$
$$= 23\,500$$
The number of eligible voters was $23\,500$.
The answer is C.

11. Solution
Since multiplication is associative, it does not matter in which order the discounts are applied;
i.e., $(0.80)(0.90)(0.95)10 = (0.80)(0.95)(0.90)10$
$$= (0.95)(0.80)(0.90)10$$
$$= (0.95)(0.90)(0.80)10$$
$$= (0.90)(0.95)(0.80)10$$
$$= (0.90)(0.80)(0.95)10$$
$$= 6.84$$
The answer is E.

12. Solution 1
Let the initial cost of living be x.
After one year it is $\frac{110}{100}x = 1.1x$.
After two years it is $\frac{110}{100}(1.1x) = 1.21x$.
After three years it is $\frac{110}{100}(1.21x) = 1.331x$.
The increase over the three years is $0.331x$.
This represents an increase of 33.1%.

Solution 2
If the initial cost of living is 100%, after three years the cost is
$(1.1)(1.1)(1.1)100\% = 133.1\%$.
This represents an increase of 33.1%.
The answer is C.

13. <u>Solution</u>

Let the original length of the patio be a and the original width be b.

The length and width of the enlarged patio are $1.1a$ and $1.1b$, respectively.

The original area is ab and the new area is $(1.1a)(1.1b) = 1.21ab$.

The increase in the area is $0.21ab$ which is a 21% increase.

The answer is C.

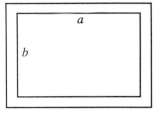

Full Solution Questions

1. <u>Solution</u>

500% of $2 = \frac{500}{100} \times 2$

$\qquad\qquad = 10$

2. <u>Solution</u>

The annual rate of interest is $\frac{180}{1200} \times 100\% = 15\%$.

3. <u>Solution</u>

Since Janet shot down 12 Invaders with 50 shots, then $\frac{12}{50} \times 100\% = 24\%$ of her shots were hits.

4. <u>Solution</u>

$\frac{10}{100}x = \frac{25}{100}(16)$

$\quad 10x = 400$

$\qquad x = 40$

5. <u>Solution 1</u>

90% capacity represents 4131 people.

10% capacity represents $4131 \div 9 = 459$ people.

100% capacity represents $10 \times 459 = 4590$ people.

<u>Solution 2</u>

Let the capacity of the hall be x people.

Then $\frac{90}{100}x = 4131$

$\qquad \frac{9}{10}x = 4131$

$$x = \frac{10}{9} \times 4131$$
$$= \frac{41310}{9}$$
$$= 4590$$

Thus, the capacity of the hall is 4590 people.

6. Solution 1
    0.08% of the tickets sold equals 2.
    1% of the tickets sold equals $\frac{2}{0.08} = \frac{200}{8} = 25$.
    100% of the tickets sold equals 2500.
    Therefore, 2500 tickets were sold.

    Solution 2
    Let the number of tickets sold be T.
    Then $\frac{0.08}{100}T = 2$
    $$0.08T = 200$$
    $$T = \frac{200}{0.08}$$
    $$= 2500$$
    Therefore, 2500 tickets were sold.

7. Solution
    One Big McBurger weighs $\frac{1}{4} \times 16 = 4$ ounces.
    Its water content is $\frac{20}{100} \times 4 = 0.8$ ounces.

8. Solution
    Let P represent the price, in cents, of the wax before tax is added.
    Then $1.05P = 120$
    $$P = \frac{120}{1.05}$$
    The new price is 70% of $P = \frac{70}{100} \times \frac{120}{1.05}$
    $$= 80 \text{ cents.}$$

9. Solution
    Sam's age is 125% or $\frac{5}{4}$ of Mary's age.
    Thus, Mary's age is $\frac{4}{5}$ or 80% of Sam's age.
    Thus, p equals 80.

10. Solution

Harry's increased salary is 110% of $360 = $\frac{110}{100} \times \$360$

$$= \$396.00.$$

His reduced work week is 90% of 44 $= \frac{90}{100} \times 44$

$$= 39.6 \text{ hours.}$$

Therefore, his new hourly salary is $\frac{396}{39.6}$ = $10.00.

11. Solution

The number of correct answers is 150% or $\frac{3}{2}$ times the number of wrong answers.

Thus, for every two wrong answers, Sue has three correct answers.

Let the number of wrong answers be $2k$.

Hence, the number of correct answers is $3k$.

Since Sue answered all 30 questions,

$3k + 2k = 30$

$5k = 30$

$k = 6$

Therefore, Sue answered 18 questions correctly.

12. Solution

Let Miss Benson's income be I.

Then Mr. Afton's income is $\frac{5}{8}I$.

Since Mr. Afton saves 40% of his income, his expenses are

60% of $\frac{5}{8}I = \frac{60}{100} \times \frac{5}{8}I$

$$= \frac{3}{8}I$$

Therefore Miss Benson's expenses are $2 \times \frac{3}{8}I = \frac{3}{4}I$.

Hence, Miss Benson saves $\frac{1}{4}I$ or 25% of her income.

13. Solution

The surface area of the original block was

$2\left[(12 \times 6) + (8 \times 6) + (12 \times 8)\right] = 2[72 + 48 + 96]$

$$= 432.$$

The reduction in surface area as a result of the cut is

twice the area of the rectangle $ABCD$ which is

$2(3 \times 9) = 54$.

The percentage decrease in the surface area is

$\frac{54}{432} \times 100\% = 12.5\%$.

Averages

Multiple Choice Questions

1. <u>Solution</u>

    The average is $\dfrac{6.2 + 0.62}{2} = \dfrac{6.82}{2}$
    $$= 3.41.$$

    The answer is C.

2. <u>Solution</u>

    The average is $\left(\dfrac{1}{2} + \dfrac{2}{3} + \dfrac{3}{4}\right) \div 3 = \left(\dfrac{6}{12} + \dfrac{8}{12} + \dfrac{9}{12}\right) \div 3$
    $$= \dfrac{23}{12} \times \dfrac{1}{3}$$
    $$= \dfrac{23}{36}.$$

    The answer is B.

3. <u>Solution</u>

    The average is $\dfrac{4.9 + 3.1 + 7.7 + 0.5 + 9.3}{5} = \dfrac{25.5}{5}$
    $$= 5.1.$$

    The answer is C.

4. <u>Solution</u>

    The average is $\left(\dfrac{2}{3} + 0.7 + \dfrac{55}{100}\right) \div 3 = \left(\dfrac{2}{3} + \dfrac{7}{10} + \dfrac{11}{20}\right) \div 3$
    $$= \dfrac{40 + 42 + 33}{60} \times \dfrac{1}{3}$$
    $$= \dfrac{115}{60} \times \dfrac{1}{3}$$
    $$= \dfrac{23}{36}.$$

    The answer is D.

5. <u>Solution</u>

    The required number is the average of $\dfrac{1}{8}$ and $\dfrac{7}{12}$.

    The number is $\left(\dfrac{1}{8} + \dfrac{7}{12}\right) \div 2 = \dfrac{3 + 14}{24} \times \dfrac{1}{2}$
    $$= \dfrac{17}{48}.$$

    The answer is E.

6. Solution

   Since the average of the two numbers is 5, their sum is $2 \times 5 = 10$.
   Since one of the numbers is –8, the other number is $10 - (-8) = 18$.
   The answer is D.

7. Solution

   Since the average of the five marks is 68, the sum of the five marks is $5 \times 68 = 340$.
   The sum of the four given marks is $75 + 62 + 84 + 53 = 274$.
   Hence, the mark of the fifth boy was $340 - 274 = 66$.
   The answer is A.

8. Solution 1

   Since the average of the three numbers is 10, the sum of the three numbers is
   $3 \times 10 = 30$.
   If one of the numbers is 5, then the sum of the remaining numbers is $30 - 5 = 25$.

   Solution 2

   Let the numbers be a, b, and 5.
   Then $\frac{a+b+5}{3} = 10$
   $$a + b + 5 = 30$$
   $$a + b = 25$$
   The sum of the remaining numbers is 25.
   The answer is D.

9. Solution 1

   The total score for the 10 games Sally bowled in March was $10 \times 190 = 1900$.
   The total score for the 4 games Sally bowled in April was $4 \times 162 = 648$.
   Her average score for the 14 games was $\frac{1900 + 648}{14} = \frac{2548}{14} = 182$.

   Solution 2

   For each game bowled in April, Sally was 28 points below her March average.
   Thus, the drop in her average as a result of the four games in April was $\frac{4 \times 28}{14} = 8$.
   The average for the 14 games was $190 - 8 = 182$.
   The answer is E.

10. Solution

    The number of games played by the Drillers was 12.
    The number of goals scored in these games was $60 + 36 = 96$.

The average number of goals scored in each game played by the Drillers was $\frac{96}{12} = 8$.
The answer is D.

11. Solution
    Let the number of integers be n.
    Since the average of these integers is 6, we have $6n = 18$.
    Thus, the number of integers in the set is three.
    The answer is A.

12. Solution
    The amount of money spent by Karen for all the popsicles was $15(10) + 10(5) = 200$
    cents.
    The average price was $\frac{200}{25} = 8$ cents.
    The answer is C.

13. Solution
    The total number of marks earned by the class of 20 students was $20 \times 66 = 1320$ and
    the total number of marks earned by the class of 30 students was $30 \times 56 = 1680$.
    The average percentage for all students was $\frac{1320 + 1680}{50} = \frac{3000}{50} = 60$.
    The answer is E.

14. Solution
    The total time spent on the 25 questions was $\left(10 \times 1\right) + \left(10 \times 2\right) + \left(5 \times 6\right) = 60$
    minutes.
    The average time spent on each question was $\frac{60}{25} = \frac{12}{5}$ minutes.
    The answer is A.

15. Solution 1
    In calculating the original average an extra 18 marks were included.
    The correct average mark is $84 - \frac{18}{6} = 81$.

    Solution 2
    In calculating the original average, the total number of marks included were
    $6 \times 84 = 504$.
    Because of the error in one of the marks, the original number of total marks is 18
    marks too many, so the correct number of total marks is $504 - 18 = 486$.
    The correct average is $\frac{486}{6} = 81$.
    The answer is D.

16. Solution

The m pens at n dollars each cost a total of mn dollars.

The n pens at m dollars each cost a total of mn dollars.

The average cost per pen is $\frac{mn + mn}{m + n} = \frac{2mn}{m + n}$ dollars.

The answer is B.

17. Solution 1

By bowling 22 points above her previous average, Mary raised her average by 1 point.

Hence, Mary's latest game was her twenty-second game.

To raise her average 1 more point in her twenty-third game, Mary must bowl 201 (i.e., 23 points above her 178 average).

Solution 2

Let the number of games included in Mary's 177 bowling average be n.

Thus $\frac{177n + 199}{n + 1} = 178$

$177n + 199 = 178n + 178$

$n = 21$

To raise her average to 179 on her twenty-third game, Mary must bowl

$(23 \times 179) - (22 \times 178) = 201$.

The answer is E.

18. Solution

Let the number of men be m and the number of women be w.

The sum of the men's ages is $35m$ and the sum of the women's ages is $25w$.

Since the average age of the entire group is 31,

$\frac{35m + 25w}{m + w} = 31$

$35m + 25w = 31m + 31w$

$4m = 6w$

$\frac{m}{w} = \frac{6}{4}$

The ratio of men to women in the group is $3 : 2$.

The answer is E.

Full Solution Questions

1. Solution

The average is $\frac{6 + 15 + 45}{3} = \frac{66}{3}$

$= 22.$

2. Solution

    Her average mark was $\dfrac{5 + 4 + 7 + 6 + 8 + 8 + 8 + 9 + 7 + 6}{10} = \dfrac{68}{10}$

    $$= 6.8.$$

3. Solution

    The average is $\dfrac{\dfrac{1}{2} + \dfrac{3}{4}}{2} = \dfrac{\dfrac{2}{4} + \dfrac{3}{4}}{2}$

    $$= \frac{5}{4} \times \frac{1}{2}$$

    $$= \frac{5}{8}.$$

4. Solution

    The numbers to be averaged are 2, 4, 6, 8, 10, 12, and 14.

    The average of these seven numbers is $\dfrac{2 + 4 + 6 + 8 + 10 + 12 + 14}{7} = \dfrac{56}{7}$

    $$= 8.$$

5. Solution

    Since the average of the five numbers is 5.1, the sum of the five numbers is

    $5 \times 5.1 = 25.5$.

    Thus, $4.9 + 3.1 + 7.7 + k + 9.3 = 25.5$

    $$25 + k = 25.5$$

    $$k = 0.5$$

6. Solution

    Since the average of the first two numbers is 10, their sum is 20.

    Since the average of the last three numbers is 15, their sum is 45.

    The average of all the five numbers is $\dfrac{20 + 45}{5} = 13$.

7. Solution

    The sum of the marks for the class of 30 students was $30 \times 68 = 2040$, and the sum of

    the marks for the class of 25 students was $25 \times 70 = 1750$.

    The average mark for all the students was $\dfrac{2040 + 1750}{55} = \dfrac{3790}{55}$

    $$= 68\tfrac{10}{11}.$$

8. Solution

    Since the average of the first two numbers is 7, their sum is 14.

    Since the average of all three numbers is 8, their sum is 24.

    The third number is $24 - 14 = 10$.

9. Solution 1
    Since the average of the two numbers is 2, their sum is 4.
    Thus, the second number is $4 - (-3) = 7$.

    Solution 2
    Let the second number be x.
    Then $\frac{-3 + x}{2} = 2$
    $$-3 + x = 4$$
    $$x = 7$$
    The second number is 7.

10. Solution
    Since the average of the ten numbers is 20, their sum is 200.
    When one number is removed, the average of the remaining nine numbers is 19 and
    their sum is $9 \times 19 = 171$.
    The number removed was $200 - 171 = 29$.

11. Solution 1
    As a result of the recording error, the average calculated was lower than the correct
    average by $\frac{50}{25} = 2$.
    The correct average for this test was $72 + 2 = 74$.

    Solution 2
    The recording error resulted in the total used when calculating the average to be
    $86 - 36 = 50$ less than it should have been.
    The correct average for the test was $\frac{(25 \times 72) + 50}{25} = \frac{25(72 + 2)}{25}$
    $$= 74.$$

12. Solution
    Pat scored a total of $4(6.5) + 5(6.4) + 9 = 26 + 32 + 9 = 67$ points.
    Her average for the ten games was $\frac{67}{10} = 6.7$ points per game.

13. Solution
    The total number of dull lunches served in five days was $5 \times 516 = 2580$.
    The number of dull lunches served on Friday was $2580 - 2068 = 512$.

14. Solution
    Bruns Wick's total score for three games was 570.

His average score for these games was $\frac{570}{3} = 190$.

His previous average per game was $190 + 9 = 199$.

15. Solution

There are $329 \div 47 = 7$ integers in the set.

For one number to be as large as possible, the remaining 6 integers must be as small as possible.

Since the integers are all positive and different, they are 1, 2, 3, 4, 5, and 97.

The remaining number is $329 - 112 = 217$.

The largest possible integer in the set is 217.

16. Solution 1

Since his longest kick was 6 m over the average, each of his other two kicks were 3 m under the average.

Thus, they were each 34 metres.

Solution 2

Let each of the other two punts be of length x m.

Then $\frac{43 + x + x}{3} = 37$

$$43 + 2x = 111$$
$$2x = 68$$
$$x = 34$$

Each of the other two punts travelled 34 metres.

17. Solution

The middle integer is 10 since the average of an odd number of consecutive integers is the middle integer.

The five integers are 8, 9, 10, 11, and 12.

The sum of the smallest and the largest is $8 + 12 = 20$.

18. Solution

Let the four marks be m_1, m_2, m_3, and m_4.

Thus, $m_1 + m_2 = 100$
$$m_2 + m_3 = 150$$
$$m_3 + m_4 = 140$$

Combining the three equations yields

$$(m_1 + m_2) - (m_2 + m_3) + (m_3 + m_4) = 100 - 150 + 140$$
$$m_1 + m_4 = 90$$

Hence, the average of the first and fourth marks is $\frac{m_1 + m_4}{2} = 45$.

Word Problems - I

Multiple Choice Questions

1. Solution

   The length of his lunch would be $400 \times 15 = 6\,000$ cm or 60 m.

   The answer is B.

2. Solution

   In 2 hours and 12 minutes, or $2\frac{1}{5}$ hours, Bill uses up $2\frac{1}{5} \times 600 = \frac{11}{5} \times 600 = 1320$ calories.

   The answer is B.

3. Solution

   John gets 3 hours sleep on each of Saturday and Sunday nights. Therefore the total number of hours sleep he gets in a full week is $(5 \times 6) + (2 \times 3) = 36$ hours.

   The answer is D.

4. Solution

   Since $\sqrt{81} = 9$, a number that is 7 less than twice the square root of 81 is $2(9) - 7 = 11$.

   The answer is B.

5. Solution

   Let the three consecutive even integers be n, $n + 2$, and $n + 4$.

   $3n = (n + 2) + (n + 4)$

   $3n = 2n + 6$

   $n = 6$

   The smallest of the three integers is 6.

   The answer is D.

6. Solution

   Since 1200 forms are required, $1200 \div 3 = 400$ sheets of paper will be used.

   The total cost is $400 \times 0.04 = \$16.00$.

   The answer is B.

7. Solution 1

   The oranges were sold at 3 for 35 cents or $4 \times 0.35 = \$1.40$ per dozen.

   Thus the profit on one dozen oranges was $1.40 - 1.32 = \$0.08$, so the profit on five dozen was \$0.40.

Solution 2

To purchase five dozen oranges at $1.32 per dozen costs $5 \times 1.32 = \$6.60$.

Selling $5 \times 12 = 60$ oranges at 3 for 35 cents brought in $\frac{60}{3} \times 0.35 = \$7.00$.

Therefore the profit was $7.00 - 6.60 = \$0.40$.

The answer is D.

8. **Solution 1**

   Since Dale ate 4 slices or $\frac{1}{3}$ of the pizza and his share of the cost was $3.40, the total

   cost of the pizza was $3 \times 3.40 = \$10.20$.

   The cost of Pat's share was $\frac{5}{12} \times 10.20 = \$4.25$.

   Solution 2

   Since Dale ate 4 slices for a cost of $3.40, the cost per slice of the pizza was
   $3.40 \div 4 = \$0.85$.

   Thus the cost of Pat's share was $5 \times 0.85 = \$4.25$.

   The answer is D.

9. **Solution 1**

   When 16 litres are added the gas tank is filled $\frac{2}{3} - \frac{1}{2} = \frac{1}{6}$ of its capacity.

   Therefore the capacity of the tank is $6 \times 16 = 96$ litres.

   Solution 2

   Let the capacity of the tank be t litres.

   Then $\frac{1}{2}t + 16 = \frac{2}{3}t$

   $$16 = \frac{1}{6}t$$

   $$t = 96$$

   Therefore the capacity of the tank is 96 litres.

   The answer is E.

10. **Solution**

    The $30 cost of a bus pass will buy 60 rides at $0.50 a ride.

    Therefore a person with a bus pass must ride at least 61 times in order to save money.

    The answer is A.

11. **Solution 1**

    Let the number of dimes that Fred has be n.

    Then he has $(n + 5)$ nickels and $2n$ pennies.

$$10n + 5(n + 5) + 2n = 76$$
$$17n + 25 = 76$$
$$17\,n = 51$$
$$n = 3$$

Therefore Fred has $3 + 5 = 8$ nickels.

Solution 2

Tabulate the possibilities:

No. of dimes	No. of nickels	No. of pennies	Amount of Money
1	6`	2	42
2	7	4	59
3	8	6	76

Therefore Fred has 8 nickels.

The answer is C.

12. Solution 1

Let x represent the number of dimes that Bob has.

Then Arin has $(x + 6)$ nickels.

$$10x + 5(x + 6) = 135$$
$$15x + 30 = 135$$
$$15x = 105$$
$$x = 7$$

Thus Bob has 7 dimes and Arin has 13 nickels.

Altogether they have 20 coins.

Solution 2

The six extra nickels that Arin has are worth 30¢.

Without these, they will each have the same number of coins and the total value of these coins is $1.05.

The value of Arin's remaining nickels is $\frac{1}{3}(1.05) = \$0.35$, and the value of Bob's dimes is $\frac{2}{3}(1.05) = \$0.70$.

Thus Arin has $7 + 6 = 13$ nickels and Bob has 7 dimes, giving a total of 20 coins.

The answer is D.

13. Solution

When the last car enters the tunnel, the engine is 2000 meters from the end of the tunnel.

Since the engine travels the 2000 metres is 30 seconds, the speed of the train is $\frac{2000}{30} = \frac{200}{3}$ metres per second.

The answer is B.

14. Solution 1
The ratio of stone to concrete in the mixture is $4 : (4 + 2 + 1) = 4 : 7$.
Therefore $\frac{4}{7} \times 350 = 200$ shovels of stone are required to make 350 shovels of concrete.

Solution 2
Let x represent the number of shovels of cement required to make 350 shovels of concrete.
Then $2x$ shovels of sand and $4x$ shovels of stone are required.
$x + 2x + 4x = 350$
$\quad\quad\quad 7x = 350$
$\quad\quad\quad\quad x = 50$
Therefore $4 \times 50 = 200$ shovels of stone are required.
The answer is A.

Full Solution Questions

1. Solution
    The prescription contained $(4 \times 5) + (3 \times 4) + (2 \times 3) + (1 \times 2) = 40$ pills.
    The total cost is $40 \times 0.50 = \$20$.

2. Solution
    Since $62 = 7 \times 8 + 6$, the number is 8.

3. Solution 1
    The value of N is $\frac{(38 + 2) - 5}{2} = \frac{19 - 5}{2} = 7$.

    Solution 2
    $2(2N + 5) = 38$
    $\quad 2N + 5 = 19$
    $\quad\quad\quad 2N = 14$
    $\quad\quad\quad\quad N = 7$
    The value of N is 7.

4. Solution
    The weight of the milk in half a glass is $370 - 290 = 80$ g.
    Therefore the weight of the milk in a full glass is 160 g.
    Thus the weight of the glass is $370 - 160 = 210$ g.

5. <u>Solution</u>

The lady buys the apples for $6 \times 1.32 = \$7.92$ for six dozen.

She sells the apples for $6 \times 12 \times 0.20 = \$14.40$.

Her profit is $14.40 - 7.92 = \$6.48$.

6. <u>Solution</u>

Since Mary buys gumballs for $15 \div 4 = 3.75$ cents each and sells them for $15 \div 3 = 5$ cents each, her profit is $5 - 3.75 = 1.25$ cents each.

To make a profit of \$3.00 she must sell $300 \div 1.25 = 240$ gumballs.

7. <u>Solution 1</u>

Anne sold the soccer ball to Bill for $\frac{5}{6} \times 24 = \$20$.

Bill sold it to Cathy for $\frac{4}{5} \times 20 = \$16$.

The price that Dave paid was $\frac{3}{4} \times 16 = \$12$.

<u>Solution 2</u>

The price that Dave paid was $\frac{3}{4} \times \frac{4}{5} \times \frac{5}{6} \times 24 = \$12$.

8 <u>Solution 1</u>

Since a \$3.50 ticket admitted two people and a \$2.00 ticket admitted only one, the 900 people were made up of 450 singles and 225 couples.

The amount of money obtained from ticket sales was

$225(3.50) + 450(2.00) = \$1687.50$.

<u>Solution 2</u>

Let the number of \$3.50 tickets sold be x. Then $2x$ people had tickets at the couples rate, and $2x$ people had tickets at the single rate.

$2x + 2x = 900$

$\quad 4x = 900$

$\quad\quad x = 225$

Thus 225 couples and 450 singles attended the dance.

The amount of money obtained from ticket sales was

$225(3.50) + 450(2.00) = \$1687.50$.

9. <u>Solution 1</u>

Al's share is $\frac{1}{10} \times 100 = \$10$ and Bob's share is $\frac{1}{5} \times 100 = \$20$.

Therefore Carl's share is the average of \$10 and \$20, namely \$15.

Hence Dave collects $100 - 10 - 20 - 15 = \$55$.

Solution 2

Carl's share is $\dfrac{\frac{1}{10} + \frac{1}{5}}{2} = \dfrac{\frac{3}{10}}{2} = \dfrac{3}{20}$ of the total.

Then Al, Bob, and Carl collect $\dfrac{1}{10} + \dfrac{1}{5} + \dfrac{3}{20} = \dfrac{9}{20}$ of the $100.

Thus Dave collects $\dfrac{11}{20} \times 100 = \$55.00$.

10. Solution

The original cost was $12 \times 4000 \times 0.32 = \$15\,360$ per year.

The revised cost was $10 \times 4000 \times 0.34 = \$13\,600$ per year.

The yearly savings were $15\,360 - 13\,600 = \$1760$.

11. Solution

Since 540 seats are in the Orchestra section, there are $1600 - 540 = 1060$ seats in the other two sections.

If 300 seats were removed from the Mezzanine, the $1060 - 300 = 760$ remaining seats would be equally divided between the Balcony and Mezzanine.

Thus the Balcony has $760 \div 2 = 380$ seats and the Mezzanine has $380 + 300 = 680$ seats.

12. Solution

Since John has exactly one fifty-cent piece and three nickels, to maximize the amount he has he should have as many quarters and as few dimes as possible.

Thus he should have four quarters and one dime to give a total of
$3(0.05) + 1(0.10) + 4(0.25) + 1(0.50) = \$1.75$.

13. Solution 1

If 4 spheres and 3 cubes weigh 37 g and 3 spheres and 4 cubes weigh 33 g, then seven spheres and seven cubes weigh $37 + 33 = 70$ g.

Therefore the combined weight of 1 sphere and 1 cube is $70 \div 7 = 10$ g.

Solution 2

Let the weight of a sphere be x grams and the weight of a cube be y grams.

$$4x + 3y = 37$$
$$3x + 4y = 33$$

Add: $7x + 7y = 70$

$\div 7$: $x + y = 10$

Therefore the combined weight of 1 sphere and 1 cube is 10 g.

14. Solution 1

In $1\frac{1}{4}$ hours, the motorcycle travelled $\frac{5}{4} \times 60 = 75$ km.

Thus, in the same time, the truck travelled $75 - 25 = 50$ km.

The average speed of the truck was $50 \div 1\frac{1}{4} = 50 \times \frac{4}{5} = 40$ km per hour.

Solution 2

Since the motorcycle was 25 km ahead of the truck after $1\frac{1}{4}$ hours, the motorcycle must have been going $25 \div 1\frac{1}{4} = 20$ km per hour faster than the truck.

Therefore the average speed of the truck was $60 - 20 = 40$ km per hour.

Ratios - I

Multiple Choice Questions

1. <u>Solution</u>
    Since $\frac{3}{4}$ of the number is 12, the number is 16.
    Then $\frac{3}{2}$ of the number is $\frac{3}{2} \times 16 = 24$.
    The answer is B.

2. <u>Solution</u>
    The model engine must be $\frac{1}{100} \times 12 = 0.12$ m or 12 cm long.
    The answer is D.

3. <u>Solution 1</u>
    The ratio 7 : 3 is equivalent to the ratio 42 : 18.
    Since $42 - 18 = 24$, the larger number is 42.

    <u>Solution 2</u>
    Let the two numbers be $7k$ and $3k$.
    $$7k - 3k = 24$$
    $$4k = 24$$
    $$k = 6$$
    The larger number is $7k = 42$.
    The answer is B.

4. <u>Solution 1</u>
    If 50 is divided into $1 + 3 + 6 = 10$ equal parts, each part is 5.
    If 50 is divided into three parts in the ratio 1 : 3 : 6, the three parts are 5, 15, and 30.
    Hence the middle part is 15.

    <u>Solution 2</u>
    Let the three parts be x, $3x$, and $5x$.
    Then $x + 3x + 5x = 50$
    $$10x = 50$$
    $$x = 5$$
    The middle part is $3x = 15$.
    The answer is B.

5. <u>Solution</u>
   Since their combined weight is $90 + 74 = 164$ pounds, the ratio of the girl's weight to their combined weight is $74 : 164$ or $37 : 82$.
   The answer is A.

6. <u>Solution</u>
   Eight cm of snow is equivalent to 0.75 cm of rain.
   Therefore one cm of snow is equivalent to $\frac{0.75}{8}$ cm of rain.
   Hence 425 cm of snow is equivalent to $425 \times \frac{0.75}{8}$ or approximately 40 cm of rain.
   The answer is D.

7. <u>Solution</u>
   Since P articles cost Q dollars, one article costs $\frac{Q}{P}$ dollars.
   The cost of R articles is $\frac{QR}{P}$ dollars.
   The answer is D.

8. <u>Solution</u>
   The number of new-seconds in a day is $10 \times 100 \times 100 = 100\,000$.
   The number of ordinary seconds in a day is $24 \times 60 \times 60 = 86\,400$.
   Therefore a new-second is $\frac{1}{100\,000}$ of a day and an ordinary second is $\frac{1}{86\,400}$ of a day.
   The ratio of a new-second to an ordinary second is $\frac{\frac{1}{100\,000}}{\frac{1}{86\,400}} = \frac{86\,400}{100\,000} = \frac{108}{125}$.
   The answer is B.

9. <u>Solution</u>
   There are 24 squares altogether.
   In order that the number of shaded squares be half the number of unshaded squares, there must be 8 shaded squares and 16 unshaded squares.
   Since 5 squares are already shaded, 3 additional squares need to be shaded.
   The answer is E.

10. <u>Solution</u>
    The points may be illustrated on a line as follows:

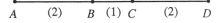

$$A \quad (2) \quad B \quad (1) \quad C \quad (2) \quad D$$

Therefore $BD = \frac{3}{5} AD$.
The answer is E.

11. <u>Solution 1</u>

The height of a tree is $\frac{45}{30}$ or 1.5 times the length of its shadow.

Thus the height of a tree with a 28 m shadow is $1.5 \times 28 = 42$ m.

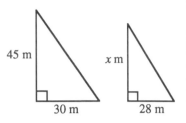

45 m x m

30 m   28 m

<u>Solution 2</u>

Let the height of the second tree be x m.

Then $\frac{x}{28} = \frac{45}{30}$

$x = \frac{(45)(28)}{30}$

$= 42$

The height of the second tree is 42 m.

The answer is A.

12. <u>Solution</u>

Since the area of $\triangle AEF$ is one-half the area of square $AEFD$, the area of $\triangle ABF$ is one-half the area of rectangle $ABCD$.

Since the area of rectangle $ABCD$ is one-half the area of the original square, the area of the shaded area is one-quarter of the area of the original square.

The answer is C.

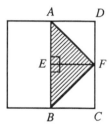

A   D

E   F

B   C

13. <u>Solution 1</u>

The ratio of the circumference to the diameter of *any* circle is $\frac{\pi d}{d} = \frac{\pi}{1}$, or $\pi : 1$.

<u>Solution 2</u>

Let the radius of the original circle be r.

Then the radius of the new circle is $r + 1$.

The ratio of the new circumference to the new diameter is $\frac{2\pi(r + 1)}{2(r + 1)} = \frac{\pi}{1}$.

The answer is C.

14. <u>Solution</u>

After the 9 gallons of wine are removed and the water is added, there are 36 gallons of wine and 9 gallons of water in the cask. At this stage, the fraction of the mixture that is wine is $\frac{36}{45} = \frac{4}{5}$.

When 9 gallons of the mixture are removed, the amount of wine removed is $\frac{4}{5} \times 9 = \frac{36}{5} = 7.2$ gallons.

Thus the final mixture contains $45 - 9 - 7.2 = 28.8$ gallons of wine and $45 - 28.8 = 16.2$ gallons of water.

The ratio of water to wine in the final mixture is $\frac{16.2}{28.8} = \frac{162}{288} = \frac{9 \times 18}{16 \times 18} = \frac{9}{16}$ or $9 : 16$.

The answer is B.

15. Solution

In the diagram, there are three concentric semicircles each with centre at 5 on the x-axis and radii 1, 3, and 5 respectively.

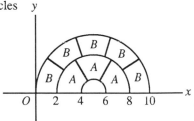

The area of the small inner semicircle is $\frac{1}{2}\pi \cdot 1^2 = \frac{1}{2}\pi$.

The area of the middle semicircle is

$$3A + \frac{1}{2}\pi = \frac{1}{2}\pi \cdot 3^2$$
$$= \frac{9}{2}\pi$$
$$3A = \frac{9}{2}\pi - \frac{1}{2}\pi$$
$$= 4\pi$$

The area of the outer semicircle is

$$5B + 3A + \frac{1}{2}\pi = \frac{1}{2}\pi \cdot 5^2$$
$$= \frac{25}{2}\pi$$
$$5B = \frac{25}{2}\pi - 4\pi - \frac{1}{2}\pi$$
$$= 8\pi$$

Therefore $\frac{3A}{5B} = \frac{4\pi}{8\pi} = \frac{1}{2}$ and $A : B = 5 : 6$.

The answer is A.

Full Solution Questions

1. Solution

Since the ratio of boys to girls is $2 : 3$, there are 12 boys and 18 girls in the class. If 6 girls join the class, the ratio of girls to boys will be $24 : 12 = 2 : 1$.

2. Solution

Frank has $\$1.83 - \$0.25 = \$1.58$ left and Janet has $\$4.99 - \$0.25 = \$4.74$ left. The ratio of the amounts they have left is $1.58 : 4.74 = 1 : 3$.

3. Solution 1
   Let the two integers be $2x$ and $5x$.
   $$(2x)(5x) = 40$$
   $$10x^2 = 40$$
   $$x^2 = 4$$
   $$x = 2 \quad \text{(since } x \text{ is a positive integer)}$$
   The larger integer is $5x = 10$.

   Solution 2
   The pairs of positive integers whose product is 40 are 1 and 40, 2 and 20, 4 and 10, and 5 and 8.
   The pair that are in the ratio 2 : 5 are 4 and 10.
   The larger integer is 10.

4. Solution
   Each side of the square is $12 \div 4 = 3$ cm. Hence the area of the square is 9 cm².
   The dimensions of the rectangle are 4 cm by 2 cm, and its area is 8 cm².
   The ratio of the area of the square to the area of the rectangle is 9 : 8.

5. Solution
   Since 1 cm on the map represents 250 000 cm on the ground, then 3.5 cm on the map represents $3.5 \times 250\,000 = 875\,000$ cm on the ground.
   Since 1 km = 100 000 cm, the distance between the towns is $\frac{875\,000}{100\,000} = 8.75$ km.

6. Solution 1
   Since 2 : 5 : 3 is equivalent to 24 : 60 : 36, the other two numbers are 24 and 36.

   Solution 2
   If the three numbers are in the ratio 2 : 5 : 3, they are of the forms $2k$, $5k$, and $3k$.
   Since $5k = 60$, $k = 12$.
   The other two numbers are 24 and 36.

   Solution 3
   Let the other two numbers be x and y.
   Then $\frac{x}{2} = \frac{60}{5} = \frac{y}{3}$.
   Hence the other two numbers are $x = 24$ and $y = 36$.

7. Solution 1
   Their win, tie, loss ratio after 10 games was 5 : 4 : 1.

At the same rates, their win, tie, loss ratio after 80 games would be 40 : 32 : 8.
Their point total after 80 would be 40(2) + 32(1) + 8(0) = 112.

Solution 2
After 10 games, the Canadiens had accumulated 5(2) + 4(1) + 1(0) = 14 points.
At the same rate, they would accumulate a total of 8(14) = 112 points after 80 games.

8. ### Solution
    Since 3 : 8 : 17 = 6 : 16 : 34, then 34 kg of potash are used in this mixture.

9. ### Solution
    Since $5^2 + 12^2 = 13^2$, the triangle is right-angled.
    The area of the triangle is $\frac{1}{2}(5)(12) = 30$ cm².
    The area of the rectangle is $6 \times 10 = 60$ cm².
    The ratio of their areas is 30 : 60 = 1 : 2.

10. ### Solution 1
    Let the height of the pole be h feet.

    Then $\frac{h}{10} = \frac{6}{2.5}$

    $h = \frac{(6)(10)}{2.5} = 24$

    The height of the pole is 24 feet.

    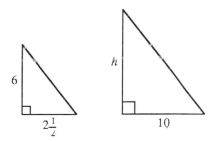

    ### Solution 2
    Since $6 : 2\frac{1}{2}$ and 24 : 10 are equivalent ratios, the height of the pole is 24 feet.

11. ### Solution
    The ratio of the surface area to the volume is $\frac{4\pi r^2}{\frac{4}{3}\pi r^3} = \frac{3r^2}{r^3} = \frac{3}{r}$.

12. ### Solution 1
    The area of square $ABCD$ is $4 \times 4 = 16$.
    The area of the triangle at each corner is
    $\frac{1}{2} \times 1 \times 3 = \frac{3}{2}$.
    The area of square $PQRS$ is $16 - 4\left(\frac{3}{2}\right) = 10$.
    The ratio of the area of $PQRS$ to the area of $ABCD$
    is 10 : 16 or 5 : 8.

    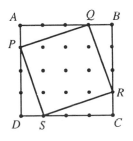

Solution 2

By the Pythagorean Theorem, in $\triangle APQ$,

$(PQ)^2 = 3^2 + 1^2$

$\qquad = 10.$

The area of $PQRS$: the area of $ABCD$

$= (PQ)^2 : (AB)^2$

$= 10 : 16$

$= 5 : 8.$

13. Solution

The total area of the four shaded triangles is

$\frac{1}{2}(4)(3) + \frac{1}{2}(4)(3) + \frac{1}{2}(3)(2) + \frac{1}{2}(5)(2)$

$= 6 + 6 + 3 + 5$

$= 20$

Since the area of the square is 25, the area of the

unshaded triangles is 5.

The ratio of the shaded area to the unshaded area is

$20 : 5 = 4 : 1.$

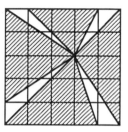

14. Solution 1

Since $\dfrac{a}{b+c} = \dfrac{2}{5}, \dfrac{b+c}{a} = \dfrac{5}{2}.$

Therefore $\dfrac{b}{a} + \dfrac{c}{a} = \dfrac{5}{2}.$

But $\dfrac{a}{b} = \dfrac{3}{4}$, so $\dfrac{b}{a} = \dfrac{4}{3}.$

Therefore $\dfrac{4}{3} + \dfrac{c}{a} = \dfrac{5}{2}$

$\qquad\qquad \dfrac{c}{a} = \dfrac{5}{2} - \dfrac{4}{3}$

$\qquad\qquad\quad = \dfrac{7}{6}$

Hence $a : c = 6 : 7.$

Solution 2

Since $a : b = 3 : 4 = 6 : 8$ and $a : (b + c) = 2 : 5 = 6 : 15,$

$a : b : (b + c) = 6 : 8 : 15.$

Therefore $a : b : (b + c) : c = 6 : 8 : 15 : 7.$

Hence $a : c = 6 : 7.$

15. <u>Solution 1</u>

Since $AB : AC = 3 : 5$,

$\qquad AB : BC = 3 : 2 = 15 : 10.$

Since $BD : CD = 7 : 2$,

$\qquad BC : CD = 5 : 2 = 10 : 4.$

Therefore $AB : BC : CD = 15 : 10 : 4.$

Multiplying each ratio by $\frac{5}{4}$ gives

$AB : BC : CD = \frac{75}{4} : \frac{50}{4} : 5.$

Thus if $CD = 5$ cm, $AB = \frac{75}{4}$ cm.

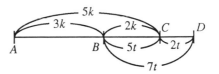

<u>Solution 2</u>

Since $BD : CD = 7 : 2$, $BC : CD = 5 : 2 = \frac{25}{2} : 5.$

Since $AB : AC = 3 : 5$, $AB : BC = 3 : 2 = \frac{3}{2} : 1.$

Therefore $AB = \frac{3}{2} \times \frac{25}{2} = \frac{75}{4}$ cm.

Circles

Multiple Choice Questions

1. <u>Solution 1</u>
   The 40 games played are represented by the area of
   a full circle.
   The number of games won, represented by the area
   in a half circle, is $\frac{1}{2}(40) = 20$.
   The number of games tied, represented by the area
   in a quarter circle, is $\frac{1}{4}(40) = 10$.
   Therefore the number of games won or tied is
   20 + 10 = 30.

   Wildcat Games

   <u>Solution 2</u>
   The number of games won or tied is (the total
   number of games) – (the number of games lost).
   The 40 games played are represented by the area of
   a full circle.
   The number of games lost, represented by the area
   in a quarter circle, is $\frac{1}{4}(40) = 10$.
   Therefore the number of games won or tied is
   40 – 10 = 30.
   The answer is D.

2. <u>Solution</u>
   The circumference of a circle is given by the formula $C = 2\pi r$.
   Therefore $2\pi r = 6\pi$
   $\qquad\qquad r = 3$
   The radius is 3.
   The answer is A.

3. <u>Solution</u>
   The area of any circle is πr^2 so the area of this circle is $\pi\left(\frac{1}{\pi}\right)^2 = \pi \times \frac{1}{\pi} \times \frac{1}{\pi} = \frac{1}{\pi}$.
   The answer is C.

4. Solution

The arc length of a semicircle is $\frac{1}{2}(2\pi r) = \pi r$.

Therefore the radius of the larger circle is 12 and the
radius of each of the smaller circles is 6.

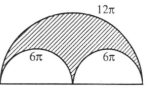

The area of a semicircular region is $\frac{1}{2}\pi r^2$.

The area of the larger semicircular region is

$\frac{1}{2}\pi(12)^2 = \frac{1}{2}\pi(144) = 72\pi$.

The area of each smaller semicircular region is

$\frac{1}{2}\pi(6)^2 = \frac{1}{2}\pi(36) = 18\pi$.

The shaded area is the area of the larger semicircular
region minus the area of the two smaller semicircular
regions.

The shaded area is $72\pi - 2(18\pi) = 72\pi - 36\pi = 36\pi$.

The answer is C.

5. Solution

The circumference of the circle is $2\pi r$, which in this case is 40 cm.

$2\pi r = 40$

$r = \frac{40}{2\pi} = \frac{20}{\pi}$

The radius is $\frac{20}{\pi}$ cm.

The answer is C.

6. Solution

If the original radius of the circle is r, then the increased radius is $2r$. (Increasing a
value by 100% changes the value from 100% to 200%, or in other words, doubles it).

The original area is πr^2 and the increased area is $\pi(2r)^2 = \pi \times 4r^2 = 4\pi r^2$.

The increase is $4\pi r^2 - \pi r^2 = 3\pi r^2$.

$3\pi r^2$ compared to the original area of πr^2, is three times as great, or 300%.

The answer is C.

7. Solution

Let the side of the square be s and let the radius of the circle be r.

Since the perimeters are equal, $4s = 2\pi r$

$s = \frac{2\pi r}{4} = \frac{\pi r}{2}$

The ratio of the area of the square to the area of the circle is

$$\frac{s^2}{\pi r^2} = \frac{\left(\frac{\pi r}{2}\right)^2}{\pi r^2}$$

$$= \frac{\left(\frac{\pi^2 r^2}{4}\right)}{\pi r^2}$$

$$= \frac{\pi^2 r^2}{4\pi r^2}$$

$$= \frac{\pi}{4}.$$

The answer is D.

8. Solution

The area of the square is 16 square units, so any
side of the square is $\sqrt{16} = 4$ units.
Therefore OC (a radius of the circle) is 4 units.
The area of the circle is $\pi r^2 = \pi(4)^2 = 16\pi$ square
units.
The answer is B.

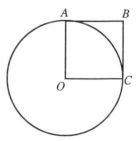

9. Solution 1

If the radii of the two circles are r_1 and r_2, the two circumferences are $2\pi r_1$ and $2\pi r_2$.
The difference of the circumferences is

$$2\pi r_1 - 2\pi r_2$$
$$= 2\pi(r_1 - r_2)$$
$$= 2\pi(10) \qquad \text{(since the difference of the radii is 10)}$$
$$= 20\pi.$$

Solution 2

Let us consider a special case where the smaller circle has radius 0 and the larger circle
has radius 10. (In general cases, specific values should produce the same results).
The circumference of the smaller circle is 0 and that of the larger circle is 20π.
Thus the difference is 20π.
The answer is C.

10. Solution

The shaded parts include one complete circle and four quarter circles.

This is the equivalent of $1 + 4\left(\frac{1}{4}\right) = 1 + 1 = 2$ complete circles.

The unshaded parts include four three quarter circles.

This is the equivalent of $4\left(\frac{3}{4}\right) = 3$ complete circles.

The ratio of the area of the shaded parts to the area of the unshaded parts is $2 : 3$.

The answer is D.

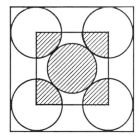

11. Solution

The area of the shaded portion is the area of the circle minus the area of the square.

The diagonal of the square is the diameter of the circle.

Therefore the radius of the circle is 1, and the area is $\pi r^2 = \pi(1)^2 = \pi$ cm².

The square is composed of four triangles each with a side of 1 cm and a height of 1 cm.

Therefore the area of the square is

$4 \times \frac{1}{2} \times 1 \times 1 = 2$ cm².

The area of the shaded portion is $(\pi - 2)$ cm².

The answer is C.

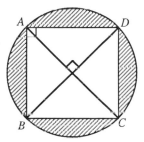

12. Solution

If the area of the square is 49 cm², then each side must be 7 cm.

The diagonal of the square is the hypotenuse of a right-angled triangle whose other sides are each 7 cm.

Using the Pythagorean Theorem,

$$(AB)^2 = 7^2 + 7^2$$
$$= 49 + 49$$
$$= 98$$

Therefore the diagonal is $\sqrt{98}$ cm.

Since this is the diameter of the circle, the radius is $\frac{\sqrt{98}}{2}$ cm.

Using approximations, $\sqrt{98} \approx 10$.

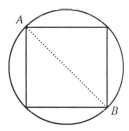

Therefore the radius is approximately $\frac{10}{2}$ = 5 cm.

Checking with the given answers, 5 is greater than $\frac{7}{2}$.

The answer is D.

Full Solution Questions

1. Solution
    The circumference of a circle is given by the formula $C = 2\pi r$.
    Since the radius is 50 m, the circumference is $2(\pi)(50) = 100\pi$ metres.

2. Solution
    If the radius of a circle is 1 unit, then the area, which is given by the formula $A = \pi r^2$,
    is $\pi(1)^2 = \pi$ square units.

3. Solution
    Since the circle just fits inside the square, the
    diameter of the circle is the same length as the side
    of the square.
    Thus the diameter is 10 cm and the radius is 5 cm.

    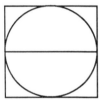

4. Solution
    The area of any circle is given by the formula $A = \pi r^2$.
    So $\pi r^2 = 9\pi$
    $r^2 = 9$
    $r = 3$
    The length of the diameter is $2(3) = 6$ cm.

5. Solution
    The semicircle has a diameter of 2 so its radius
    is 1.
    The arc length of the semicircular top is
    $\frac{1}{2}(2)(\pi)(1) = \pi$ feet.
    The perimeter of the window is $\pi + 3 + 2 + 3$
    $= (\pi + 8)$ feet.

    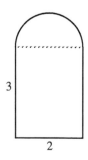

6. <u>Solution</u>
The shaded area consists of four quarter circles
which is the equivalent to one of the original circles.
The unshaded area consists of four three quarter
circles which is the equivalent to $4\left(\frac{3}{4}\right) = 3$ original
circles.
Therefore the ratio of the area of the shaded parts to
the area of the unshaded portions is 1 : 3.

7. <u>Solution</u>
The side of the square is the same length as the
diameter of the circle, which is 10 units.
The area of the square is (10)(10) = 100 square
units.
The area of the circle is $\pi r^2 = \pi(5)^2 = \pi(25) = 25\pi$
square units.
Therefore the ratio of the area of the square to the
area of the circle is $\frac{100}{25\pi} = \frac{4}{\pi}$ or 4 : π.

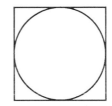

8. Solution
The shaded area is the area of the square *ABCD*
minus the area of a quarter circle.
The area of the square is $1^2 = 1$.
The area of a quarter circle is $\frac{1}{4}\pi(1)^2 = \frac{\pi}{4}$.
Therefore the shaded area is $1 - \frac{\pi}{4}$.

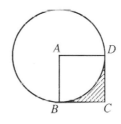

9. <u>Solution</u>
Since no lengths are given, let us
assume the length of *AB* is *x* units.
Each of the upper two semicircles has
diameter 2*x*.
Therefore the length of the upper path is
$\frac{1}{2}(2)(\pi)(x) + \frac{1}{2}(2)(\pi)(x) = 2\pi x$.
The lower semicircles have diameters of
3*x* and *x* units respectively.

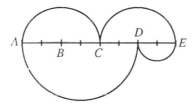

Therefore the length of the lower path is

$\frac{1}{2}(2)(\pi)\left(\frac{3x}{2}\right) + \frac{1}{2}(2)(\pi)\left(\frac{x}{2}\right)$

$= \frac{3\pi x}{2} + \frac{\pi x}{2}$

$= \frac{4\pi x}{2}$

$= 2\pi x$

Hence the ratio of the lengths of the two paths is
$2\pi x : 2\pi x$ or $1 : 1$.

10. <u>Solution</u>

The shaded region is the area of the semicircle
minus the area of the right-angled triangle ABC.
The area of the right-angled triangle ABC is
$\frac{1}{2}(AC)(CB) = \frac{1}{2}(8)(6) = 24$.

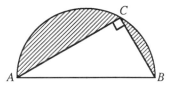

To find the area of the semicircle we must know
the radius.
Using the Pythagorean Theorem,

$(AB)^2 = (AC)^2 + (CB)^2$

$\qquad = (8)^2 + (16)^2$

$\qquad = 64 + 36$

$\qquad = 100$

Therefore $AB = 10$.
Therefore the radius of the circle is 5.
The area of the semicircle is $\frac{1}{2}\pi(5)^2 = \frac{25\pi}{2}$.
The shaded area is $\frac{25\pi}{2} - 24 = \frac{25\pi - 48}{2}$.

11. <u>Solution</u>

The total distance travelled by each wheel is 2 km = 2 × 1000 metres

$= 2 \times 1000 \times 100$ cm.

The circumference of each wheel is $\pi d = \pi(60) = 60\pi$ cm.
The number of rotations the wheel must have made is

$\frac{200\,000}{60\pi} \cong \frac{200\,000}{200} = 1000$.

12. <u>Solution</u>

ABCD is a rectangle, so the diameter of the
circumscribing circle is the diagonal of the rectangle.

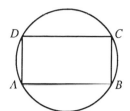

$(AC)^2 = (AB)^2 + (BC)^2$

$= (8)^2 + (6)^2$

$= 64 + 36$

$= 100$

Therefore $AC = 10$.

The radius of the circle is $\frac{10}{2} = 5$ cm.

The area of the circle is $\pi r^2 = \pi(5)^2 = 25\pi$ cm^2.

2-Dimensional Geometry - I

Multiple Choice Questions

1. <u>Solution</u>
    Since $AB = AC$, $\triangle ABC$ is isosceles and
    $\angle B = \angle C$.
    But $\angle B + \angle C = 180° - 50° = 130°$.
    Therefore $\angle B = 65°$.
    The answer is D.

    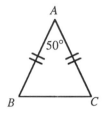

2. <u>Solution 1</u>
    Since c and $60°$ are opposite angles, $c = 60°$.

    <u>Solution 2</u>
    Since $c + 40° + 80° = 180°$,
    therefore $c = 60°$.
    The answer is B.

    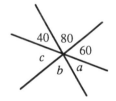

3. <u>Solution</u>
    Each of p, q, r, s, and t is equal to
    $360° - 324° = 36°$.
    Therefore their sum is $5(36°) = 180°$.
    The answer is E.

    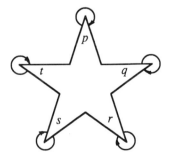

4. <u>Solution</u>
    Divide the hexagon into four triangles by
    drawing diagonals AE, AD, and AC.
    Since the sum of the angles in each triangle
    is $180°$, the sum of the angles in the
    hexagon is $4 \times 180° = 720°$
    The answer is D.

5. <u>Solution</u>

Each hour the minute hand rotates through $360°$.

Each minute the minute hand rotates through $360° \div 60 = 6°$.

From 9:45 to 10:13 is 28 minutes, so the minute hand passes through $28 \times 6° = 168°$.

The answer is B.

6. <u>Solution 1</u>

Since $AB = BC = 3$, $CD = 2$.

The area of $\triangle ABD$ is $\frac{1}{2}(5)(3) = \frac{15}{2}$.

The area of $\triangle ABC$ is $\frac{1}{2}(3)(3) = \frac{9}{2}$.

The area of $\triangle ACD$ is $\frac{15}{2} - \frac{9}{2} = 3$.

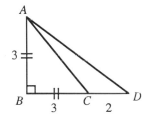

<u>Solution 2</u>

The area of $\triangle ACD$ is $\frac{1}{2}(CD)(AB) = \frac{1}{2}(2)(3)$
$$= 3.$$

The answer is B.

7. <u>Solution</u>

Since $\triangle PQT$ is right-angled, then, by the Pythagorean Theorem,

$PT = \sqrt{(PQ)^2 + (QT)^2}$
$= \sqrt{64 + 36}$
$= \sqrt{100}$
$= 10$

Similarly,

$TS = \sqrt{(TR)^2 + (RS)^2}$
$= \sqrt{9 + 16}$
$= \sqrt{25}$
$= 5$

Therefore $PS = 10 + 5 = 15$ cm.

The answer is C.

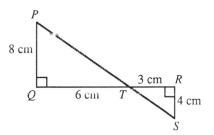

8. Solution
    By the Pythagorean Theorem,
    $BC = \sqrt{(BD)^2 - (DC)^2}$
    $\quad = \sqrt{25 - 9}$
    $\quad = \sqrt{16}$
    $\quad = 4$
    Therefore $AB = AC - BC$
    $\qquad\qquad = 12 - 4$
    $\qquad\qquad = 8$
    The top of the ladder is 8 m from the top of the wall.
    The answer is C.

    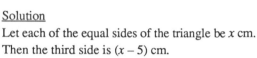

9. Solution
    Let each of the equal sides of the triangle be x cm.
    Then the third side is $(x - 5)$ cm.
    Since the perimeter is 31 cm,
    $$x + x + x - 5 = 31$$
    $$3x = 36$$
    $$x = 12$$
    Each of the equal sides is 12 cm long.
    The answer is B.

10. Solution
    Since the square is folded in half, the width of the
    rectangle is one-half its length.
    Since the perimeter of the rectangle is 18 cm, its
    length and width are 6 cm and 3 cm, respectively.
    Therefore the area of the square is $6 \times 6 = 36$ cm².
    The answer is E.

    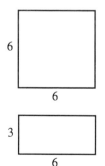

11. Solution
    When reflected in the x-axis, the image of each
    rectangle is a rectangle on the opposite side of the
    x-axis and at the same distance from the axis as the
    original rectangle.
    The answer is D.

    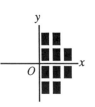

12. Solution

Each side of the room is $10 \times 100 = 1000$ cm long.

Hence $1000 \div 50 = 20$ tiles are required to go along one side of the room.

Therefore $20 \times 20 = 400$ tiles are required to cover the floor.

The answer is A.

13. Solution

The four lines from A will divide the triangle into five sections.

If one line is drawn from B it will divide each of the sections in two.

Hence four lines from B will divide each of the sections into five sections.

Therefore there are $5 \times 5 = 25$ sections.

The answer is B.

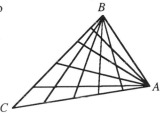

14. Solution

Draw perpendiculars from A and D to E and F on BC. Then $AE = DF = 5$.

Let $AB = AD = DC = x$.

Therefore $EF = x$ and since BC is 2 less than the sum of AB, AD, and DC, it follows that

$BE = FC = x - 1$

By the Pythagorean Theorem,

$x^2 = (x - 1)^2 = 5^2$.

But $13^2 - 12^2 = 5^2$.

Therefore $x = 13$ and $x - 1 = 12$.

The area of trapezoid $ABCD$

$= ABE + AEFD + DFC$

$= \frac{1}{2}(12)(5) + (13)(5) + \frac{1}{2}(12)(5)$

$= 30 + 65 + 30$

$= 125$

The answer is D.

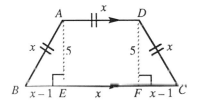

Full Solution Questions

1. <u>Solution</u>

   Since the window panes are identical, each of the
   angles at O is $\frac{1}{5} \times 180° = 36°$.

   Therefore $\angle RON = 36°$.

   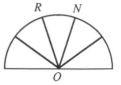

2. <u>Solution</u>

   Since BCD is a straight angle and $\angle ACD = 130°$,
   then $\angle ACB = 50°$.
   Since $AB = AC$, $\triangle ABC$ is isosceles and
   $\angle B = \angle ACB = 50°$.
   Therefore $\angle A = 180° - 50° - 50°$
   $ = 80°$.

   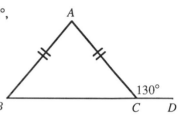

3. <u>Solution</u>

   Since ACE is a triangle, $\angle A + \angle C + \angle E = 180°$.
   Since BDF is a triangle, $\angle B + \angle D + \angle F = 180°$.
   Therefore $\angle A + \angle C + \angle E + \angle B + \angle D + \angle F$
   $ = 180° + 180°$
   $ = 360°$.

   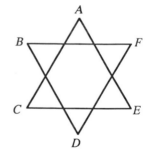

4. <u>Solution</u>

   Let angle A be x degrees.
   Then angle B is $(x + 36)$ degrees and angle C is
   $6x$ degrees.
   Therefore $x + (x + 36) + 6x = 180$
   $ 8x + 36 = 180$
   $ 8x = 144$
   $ x = 18$
   Hence angle A is 18 degrees.

   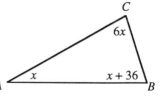

5. Solution 1

   Join AC and AD, dividing the pentagon into three triangles.

   Since the sum of the angles in a triangle is $180°$, the sum of the angles in the three triangles is $3 \times 180° = 540°$.

   Therefore the sum of the angles in the pentagon is $540°$.

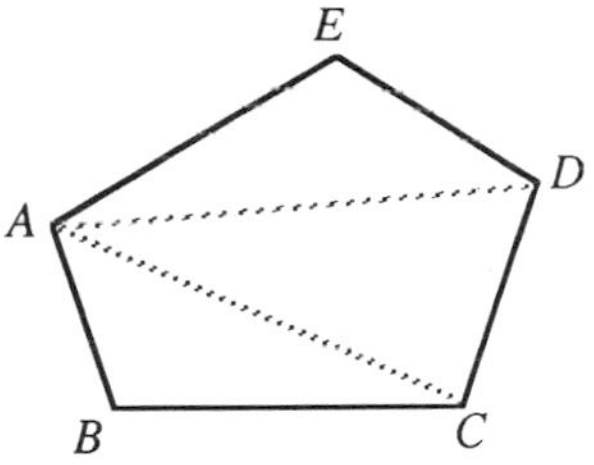

   Solution 2

   Let P be any point inside the pentagon. Join P to each of the vertices of the pentagon, creating five triangles.

   The sum of the angles in all five triangles is $5 \times 180° = 900°$.

   But the sum of all the angles about P is $360°$.

   Therefore the sum of the angles in the pentagon is $900° - 360° = 540°$.

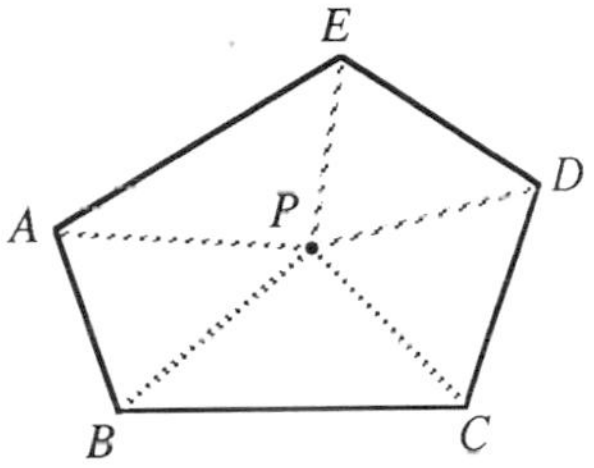

6. Solution

   The area of $\triangle ACD$ is $\frac{1}{2}(\text{base} \times \text{height})$

   $$= \frac{1}{2}(AD)(BC)$$

   $$= \frac{5}{2}BC$$

   Therefore $\frac{5}{2}BC = 15$

   $$BC = 6$$

   The area of $\triangle ABC$ is $\frac{1}{2}(AB)(BC)$

   $$= \frac{1}{2}(9)(6)$$

   $$= 27.$$

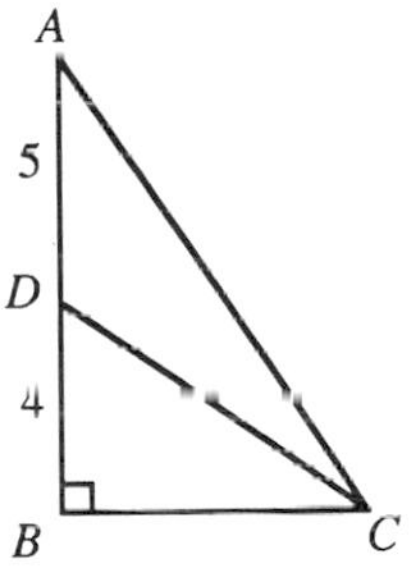

7. Solution

   In the diagram, AB represents the wall, BC represents the moat, and AC represents the ladder.

   By the Pythagorean Theorem, $AC^2 = AB^2 + BC^2$.

   Therefore $AB^2 = AC^2 - BC^2$

   $$= 169 - 25$$

   $$= 144$$

   Hence $AB = 12$.

   The height of the wall is 12 metres.

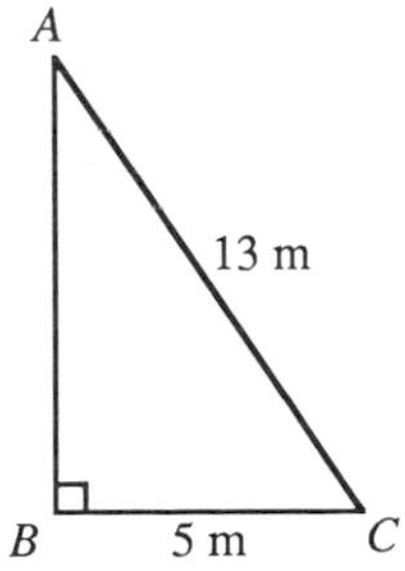

8. Solution

In the diagram, if we draw AE parallel to BC, then
$AE = 12$ and $EC = 10$.
Since $DC = 15$, $DE = 5$.
By the Pythagorean Theorem,

$$AD^2 = AE^2 + DE^2$$
$$= 144 + 25$$
$$= 169$$

Therefore $AD = 13$.
The distance between the tops of the poles is 13 metres.

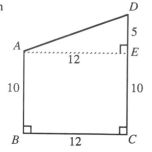

9. Solution

Since the hexagon is regular, the diagonals
NR, PS, and QT intersect at a point O
forming 6 equilateral triangles.
Since the perimeter of the hexagon is 42
cm, each side is 7 cm.
Therefore $NR = NO + OR$

$$= 7 + 7$$
$$= 14 \text{ cm.}$$

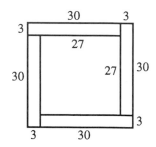

10. Solution

The measure of each side of the inner
square is $30 - 3 = 27$ cm.
The area of the inner square is
$27 \times 27 = 729 \text{ cm}^2$.

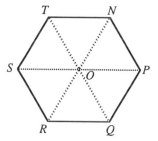

11. Solution

Since each object requires 6 bolts and nuts, she will
be able to make $60 \div 6 = 10$ objects.
At this point she will have lots of short and long
pieces left over but no bolts or nuts.

nut and bolt

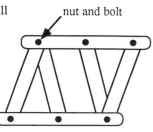

12. Solution

The perimeter of the triangle is $13 - 2 = 11$ cm.

Since the sum of any two sides of a triangle is greater than the third side, the only possible triangles we can form have sides of lengths 1, 5, 5 or 2, 4, 5 or 3, 3, 5 or 3, 4, 4, with all lengths being in centimetres.

Hence the longest possible side of the triangle is 5 cm.

13. Solution

The area of the cross is $5 \times 1 = 5$ cm².

Hence the area of the square formed by the pieces of the cross is also 5 cm².

Each side of the square is $\sqrt{5}$ cm.

14. Solution 1

Since the length of the floor is 1500 cm, $1500 \div 25 = 60$ tiles will be required to do a row along the length of the floor.

Since the width of the floor is 800 cm, $800 \div 25 = 32$ tiles will be required to do a row across the width of the floor.

Thus a total of $60 \times 32 = 1920$ tiles will be needed.

Solution 2

The area of the floor is $15 \times 8 = 120$ m².

Each tile covers an area of $\frac{1}{4} \times \frac{1}{4} = \frac{1}{16}$ m².

Hence a total of $120 \div \frac{1}{16} = 120 \times 16 = 1920$ tiles will be needed.

Number Patterns and Sequences - I

Multiple Choice Questions

1. <u>Solution</u>
   If the digits are arranged in descending order, we get 9541.
   If the digits are arranged in ascending order, we get 1459.
   The difference between these numbers is 8082.
   The answer is D.

2. <u>Solution</u>
   The sum is $8 + 16 + 24 + 32 + 40 + 48 = 168$.
   The answer is C.

3. <u>Solution</u>
   Since $12\,291 = (512 \times 24) + 3$, then $12\,291$ hours is 512 days plus 3 hours.
   The time will be 3 hours later than 10:00 a.m., or 1:00 p.m.
   The answer is B.

4. <u>Solution</u>
   The numbers in the sequence 777, 770, 763, ... are all multiples of 7.
   The only answer that is a multiple of 7 is 42.
   The answer is D.

5. <u>Solution 1</u>
   The first sequence is 2, 7, 12, 17, 22, 27, 32, 37, 42, 47, 52, 57, ...
   The second sequence is 3, 10, 17, 24, 31, 38, 45, 52, 59, ...
   The second number that occurs in both sequences is 52.

   <u>Solution 2</u>
   The number that next occurs in both sequences will be the seventh number after 17 in the first sequence and the fifth number after 17 in the second sequence.
   This number is $17 + (7 \times 5) = 52$.
   The answer is B.

6. <u>Solution</u>

$$\frac{190 + 192 + 194 + 196 + 198 - 200 - 202 - 204 - 206 - 208}{10}$$

$$= \frac{(190 - 200) + (192 - 202) + (194 - 204) + (196 - 206) + (198 - 208)}{10}$$

$$= \frac{-10 - 10 - 10 - 10 - 10}{10}$$

$$= \frac{-50}{10}$$

$$= -5$$

The answer is B.

7. <u>Solution</u>

$1 - 2 + 3 - 4 + 5 - 6 + ... + 99 - 100$
$= (1 - 2) + (3 - 4) + (5 - 6) + ... + (99 - 100)$
$= -1 - 1 - 1 - 1 - ... - 1$
$= -50$, since there are 50 pairs of numbers each with a sum of -1.
The answer is A.

8. <u>Solution</u>

The bottom row of the pattern for the seventh triangular number has 7 circles.
Thus the pattern has a total of $7 + 6 + 5 + 4 + 3 + 2 + 1 = 28$ circles.
The seventh triangular number is 28.
The answer is B.

9. <u>Solution</u>

Each cut produces twice the number of pieces of paper as the previous cut.
Thus, 1 cut produces 2 pieces of paper.

2 cuts produce $2^2 = 4$ pieces of paper.

3 cuts produce $2^3 = 8$ pieces of paper.

$. . .$

10 cuts produce $2^{10} = 1024$ pieces of paper.
Since each piece of paper is 0.01 mm thick, the height of the pile is
$1024 \times 0.01 = 10.24$ mm or 1.024 cm.
The answer is C.

10. Solution

Using the given pattern,

$$\sqrt{1^3 + 2^3 + 3^3 + 4^3 + 5^3 + 6^3 + 7^3 + 8^3 + 9^3 + 10^3}$$
$$= \sqrt{(1 + 2 + 3 + 4 + 5 + 6 + 7 + 8 + 9 + 10)^2}$$
$$= 1 + 2 + 3 + 4 + 5 + 6 + 7 + 8 + 9 + 10$$
$$= 55$$

The answer is C.

11. Solution

The second row is 4 3 2 1.

The one diagonal is 4 2 1 3 as illustrated.

It follows that the second column must be 2 3 1 4.

The sum of the numbers in the two squares marked with an asterisk is $3 + 4 = 7$.

The answer is E.

1	2	3	4
4	3	2	1
	1		
3	4		

12. Solution

Since K is the eleventh letter in the alphabet and there is one letter in the first column, three in the second, five in the third column, and so on, then there will be 21 letters in the "K" column.

The answer is D.

13. Solution

All the integers in column Q are multiples of 6.

Since 996 is a multiple of 6 it will occur in column Q.

Since all integers that are four more than a multiple of 6 occur in column T, then 1000 will appear in column T.

The answer is E.

Full Solution Questions

1. Solution

$$3 + 6 + 9 + 12 + 15 + 18 + 21 + 24 + 27 + 30$$
$$= 3 \times 1 + 3 \times 2 + 3 \times 3 + 3 \times 4 + ... + 3 \times 10$$
$$= 3 \times (1 + 2 + 3 + 4 + ... + 10)$$
$$= 3 \times 55$$
$$= 165$$

2. Solution

In this pattern, known as "Pascal's Triangle", each row begins and ends with a 1 and each of the other numbers in the row is obtained by adding the two numbers above it in the preceding row. For example, in the fifth row, the 6 is obtained by adding the two threes above it.

Thus, the second number in the rows after the first row form the sequence 1, 2, 3, 4, ...

Hence, the second number in the fifteenth row is 14.

3. Solution

The sum of each row, column, or diagonal is $10 + 9 + 14 = 33$.

Then the number in the middle square is 11, and the number in the lower right corner is 12.

It follows that the value of N is 7.

10		
9	11	13
14	N	12

4. Solution 1

Time	4:00	4:10	4:20	4:30	4:40	4:50	5:00
No. of cells	5	10	20	40	80	160	320

There were 320 cells in the dish at the end of one hour.

Solution 2

Since there are 6 ten-minute intervals in an hour, the number of cells will double 6 times.

Therefore, at the end of one hour, there will be $5 \times 2^6 = 5 \times 64 = 320$ cells in the dish.

5. Solution

The sequence of heights that the ball travels is 16, 8, 8, 4, 4, 2, 2, 1.

The total distance the ball had travelled is $16 + 8 + 8 + 4 + 4 + 2 + 2 + 1 = 45$ metres.

6. Solution

Between 500 and 600 there are eight integers in which the sum of the digits is 12, namely 507, 516, 525, 534, 543, 552, 561, and 570.

Between 600 and 700 there are seven more such integers, namely 606, 615, 624, 633, 642, 651, and 660.

Thus there are 15 integers between 500 and 700 in which the sum of the digits is 12.

7. Solution

Since all multiples of 4 occur in column c, and $1000 = 4 \times 250$, then 1000 will occur in column c.

Multiples of 8 occur in rows in which the numbers go from right to left.

Since 1000 is also a multiple of 8, 1001 will be in column b.

8. Solution

    Let a_n represent the nth number in the sequence.

    Since $a_7 = a_6 + a_5$, then $a_5 = a_7 - a_6$

    $$= 47 - 29$$
    $$= 18$$

    Similarly, $a_4 = a_6 - a_5$

    $$= 29 - 18$$
    $$= 11$$

    Therefore, $a_3 = a_5 - a_4$

    $$= 18 - 11$$
    $$= 7$$

    The third number in the sequence is 7.

9. Solution

    The sequence of steps taken to reach the tree is 2, –1, 2, –1, 2, –1, 2, –1, 2, –1, 2.

    The sum of these terms is 7, but the total number of steps is $(6 \times 2) + (5 \times 1) = 17$.

    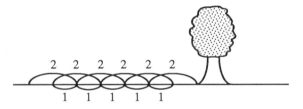

10. Solution

    For the first nine pages a total of 9 digits was used.

    For pages 10 to 99 a total of $2 \times 90 = 180$ digits was used.

    Thus, up to page 99, a total of 189 digits was used, leaving $216 - 198 = 27$ digits to be used.

    These 27 digits were sufficient to number 9 more pages with 3-digit numbers.

    Hence the number of pages in the book is $9 + 90 + 9 = 108$.

11. Solution

    To write the numbers from 1 to 9, Martina used 9 digits.

    To write the numbers from 10 to 99, she used $2 \times 90 = 180$ digits.

    The $288 - 189 = 99$ remaining digits resulted from writing three-digit numbers.

    Since 99 digits will produce 33 three-digit numbers, starting at 100, the last number she had written was 132.

12. Solution

Since the sum of two consecutive integers is odd, they cannot add to 1000.

Let three consecutive integers whose sum is 1000 be n, $n + 1$, and $n + 2$.

$$n + (n + 1) + (n + 2) = 1000$$
$$3n = 997$$
$$n = 332\frac{1}{3} \text{ which is not an integer.}$$

Consider four consecutive integers whose sum is 1000.

$$n + (n + 1) + (n + 2) + (n + 3) = 1000$$
$$4n = 994$$
$$n = 248\frac{1}{2} \text{ which is not an integer.}$$

However, five consecutive integers can add to 1000 since

$n + (n + 1) + (n + 2) + (n + 3) + (n + 4) = 1000$ gives $5n = 990$ or $n = 198$ which is an integer.

The five consecutive integers are 198, 199, 200, 201, and 202.

13. Solution

The number of integers used in the first five rows is $1 + 2 + 3 + 4 + 5 = 15$.

The number of integers used in the first 60 rows is

$$1 + 2 + 3 + 4 + ... + 58 + 59 + 60$$
$$= (1 + 60) + (2 + 59) + (3 + 58) + ... + (30 + 31)$$
$$= 61 + 61 + 61 + ... + 61$$
$$= 30 \times 61$$
$$= 1830$$

Therefore the first number in the 61st row is 1831.

The 23rd number in this row is $1831 + 22 = 1853$.

Counting and Logic - I

Multiple Choice Questions

1. <u>Solution</u>
   If the numbers are placed on a number line, the arrangement would be

   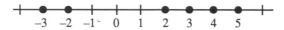

   $3 > 2$ is true.
   $-3 < -2$ is true.
   $2 > -3$ is true.
   $-2 < -3$ is false.
   $5 \neq 4$ is true.
   The only false statement is $-2 < -3$.
   The answer is D.

2. <u>Solution</u>
   The number of unit spaces from J to L on the given scale is $93 - 18 = 75$.
   The distance from J to K is $\frac{2}{3} \times 75 = 50$.
   The number located at K must be $18 + 50 = 68$.
   The answer is D.

3. <u>Solution</u>
   A matching pair of socks consists of two of the same colour.
   If only two of the socks are pulled out they may be of different colours.
   However, if a third sock is pulled out, it must match either a blue or a grey sock.
   Hence pulling out three socks will guarantee a matching pair.
   The answer is B.

4. <u>Solution</u>
   The number of days from June 3 to June 30 (inclusive) is 28.
   Therefore the number of days from June 30, 1974 to June 3, 1975 is $365 - 28 = 337$
   days. There is no leap year day included in this period.
   The answer is A.

5. <u>Solution</u>
   Since a triomino consists of three squares, only patterns that contain a number of
   squares that is a multiple of three are possible.
   This eliminates patterns B and C.

By their configurations, patterns A and D are impossible.
Only pattern E may be made with triominoes.
One such possible arrangement is shown.

The answer is E.

6. Solution

Team	Games Played	Wins	Losses	Ties	Points
Drillers	12	8	3	1	$8 \times 2 + 1 = 17$
Blizzard	12	7	3	2	$7 \times 2 + 2 = 16$
Kickers	12	4	4	4	$4 \times 2 + 4 = 12$
Flames	12	3	7	2	$3 \times 2 + 2 = 8$
White Caps	12	3	8	1	$3 \times 2 + 1 = 7$

The answer is B.

7. Solution 1

$$\begin{array}{r} P8 \\ 3Q \\ \hline \end{array}$$
The product is $\overline{2730}$

Since $8Q$ ends in a zero, Q must be a 5 (0 is not allowed).
Since $P8$ multiplied by 35 gives the first two digits as 27, P must be either 8 or 7.
Testing shows P is 7, Q is 5.

Solution 2
Since $8Q$ ends in a zero, Q must be a 5 (0 is not allowed).
Therefore $3Q = 35$, and, since $2730 \div 35 = 78$, hence $P8 = 78$ so $P = 7$.
The answer is E.

8. Solution 1
In a non-leap year, there are 365 days which is 52 weeks plus one day. In a leap year, there is one extra day or 52 weeks plus two days.
Jan. 1, 1986 occurred on a Wednesday, Jan. 1, 1987 occurred on a Thursday, Jan. 1,

1988 occurred on a Friday, and Jan. 1, 1989 will occur on a Sunday (since 1988 has the extra day for a leap year). Jan. 1, 1990 will occur on a Monday, Jan. 1, 1991 will occur on a Tuesday, and Jan. 1, 1992 will occur on a Wednesday.

Solution 2

From Jan. 1, 1986 to Jan. 1, 1992 is six years, one of which is a leap year (1988).
The total number of days between these dates is $365 \times 5 + 366 = 2191$.
To find out the number of weeks that have passed, divide the number of days by 7 $(2191 \div 7 = 313)$. The remainder of zero shows that an exact number of weeks have passed, so Jan. 1, 1992 will fall on the same day of the week as Jan. 1, 1986.
Therefore Jan. 1, 1992 will fall on a Wednesday.
The answer is B.

9. Solution
    In order that the ends come out the holes as shown, there must be exactly two pieces of string on the underside leading to these holes (one to each hole).
    All diagrams except (E) have this property, so (E) cannot be the configuration on the underside.
    The answer is E.

10. Solution
    If Jason had one extra marble, then the number of marbles would have to be divisible by 4, 5, and 7.
    The smallest number divisible by 4, 5, and 7 is $4 \times 5 \times 7 = 140$.
    The least number of marbles that Jason could have had was $140 - 1 = 139$.
    The answer is C.

11. Solution 1
    There are two sets of couples.
    Either couple could sit at the left hand end and the other at the right hand end. Thus there are two arrangements of couples.
    The members of each couple could now interchange, each creating twice as many arrangements.
    Thus the number of arrangements is $2 \times 2 \times 2 = 8$.

Solution 2

If the couples are a_1, a_2, and b_1, b_2, they can be seated in the manner shown below, so that the members of each couple remain together.

$$a_1\ a_2\ b_1\ b_2$$
$$a_1\ a_2\ b_2\ b_1$$
$$a_2\ a_1\ b_1\ b_2$$
$$a_2\ a_1\ b_2\ b_1$$
$$b_1\ b_2\ a_1\ a_2$$
$$b_1\ b_2\ a_2\ a_1$$
$$b_2\ b_1\ a_1\ a_2$$
$$b_2\ b_1\ a_2\ a_1$$

There are 8 arrangements.

The answer is E.

12. Solution

The number of squares with one unit to a side is 24.
The number of squares with two units to a side is 15.
The number of squares with three units to a side is 8.
The number of squares with four units to a side is 3.
The number of squares with five units to a side is 0.
The total number of squares is $24 + 15 + 8 + 3 = 50$.

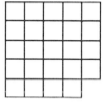

Note: If the figure had been complete, with no square missing, the number of squares would have been $25 + 16 + 9 + 4 + 1 = 55$.
Since the one square is omitted, it removes one square of <u>each</u> of the various sizes.
Hence the number of squares would have been $55 - 5 = 50$.

The answer is E.

13. Solution

There are five short pieces of chain and seemingly it would require four links to be cut and welded again to unite the pieces.

However, if one set of three links has each link cut, these three links could be used to connect the remaining four short pieces.

Hence it only requires that three links be cut and welded, so the cost is

$$3 \times 10\text{¢} + 3 \times 25\text{¢} = \$1.05.$$

The answer is C.

14. Solution

If Tanya has four extra dimes, this amounts to 40¢.

The remaining $4.10 would have to be made up of an equal number of dimes and quarters. However $\frac{410}{10 + 25}$ is not a whole number.

Therefore there could not be four extra dimes.

If Cecile has four extra quarters, this amounts to $1.00.

The remaining $3.50 is made up of an equal number of dimes and quarters.

Since $\frac{350}{10 + 25} = 10$, Tanya has 10 dimes and Cecile has 10 + 4 = 14 quarters.

They have 10 + 14 = 24 coins together.

The answer is B.

Full Solution Questions

1. Solution

The hundreds digit must be 3.

The sum of the three digits must be 15.

Hence the sum of the tens digit and the units digit is 12.

Since the units digit must be odd, it can only be 1, 3, 5, 7, or 9.

If the units digit were 1, the tens digit would be 11, which is impossible.

The units digit cannot be 3 since all digits are different.

If the units digit were 5, the tens digit would be 7. But this number would be 375 which is not in the given range.

If the units digit were 7, the tens digit would be 5 creating the number 357.

If the units digit were 9, the tens digit would be 3, causing a repeated digit.

Thus the only number is 357.

2. Solution

The largest number that can be formed from the digits 4, 7, 9, and 5 is 9754.

The smallest such number is 4579.

The sum of these is 9754 + 4579 = 14 333.

3. Solution

From 6:14 a.m. to 7:00 a.m. is 46 minutes.

From 7:00 a.m. to 8:00 p.m. is 13 hours.

From 8:00 p.m. to 8:02 p.m. is 2 minutes.

Hence from 6:14 a.m. to 8:02 p.m. the elapsed time is 13 hours 48 minutes.

4.   <u>Solution</u>
     The maximum occurs when no more than two lines
     intersect in any one point.
     There are six distinct points of intersection.
     <u>Note</u>: An interesting pattern arises, for the number
     of points of intersection, if the number of distinct
     straight lines is increased.

5.   <u>Solution</u>
     When two ordinary dice are rolled, there are 36 different outcomes, since for each of
     the six numbers rolled on the black die, any one of six outcomes may occur on the
     white die.
     Of the 36 outcomes, those that produce a sum of 7 are
     (6B + 1W, 5B + 2W, 4B + 3W, 3B + 4W, 2B + 5W, 1B + 6W).
     There are 6 ways of rolling an outcome with a sum of seven.

6.   <u>Solution</u>
     To saw the first log into 4 smaller logs required only 3 cuts.
     Thus each cut must take $\frac{9}{3} = 3$ seconds.
     To saw the second log into five smaller logs would require 4 cuts or $4 \times 3 = 12$
     seconds.

7.   <u>Solution</u>
     To be both a cube and a square of an integer, this integer must be a sixth power of an
     integer.
     Those integers which fit this pattern are 1^6, 2^6, 3^6, etc.
     These integers are $1, 2 \times 2 \times 2 \times 2 \times 2 \times 2 = 64, 3 \times 3 \times 3 \times 3 \times 3 \times 3 = 729$, etc.
     $64 = \left(2^2\right)^3 = \left(2^3\right)^2 = 4^3 = 8^2$.
     $729 = \left(3^2\right)^3 = \left(3^3\right)^2 = 9^3 = 27^2$.
     The next larger integer is 64.

8.   <u>Solution</u>
     To lose 24 hours, the watch will lose 24×60 minutes or $24 \times 60 \times 60$ seconds.
     Since one second is lost per day, this number is the number of days required.
     The number of years will be $\dfrac{24 \times 60 \times 60}{365} = 236.7$.
     An approximation is 240 years.

9. Solution
    Since each line totals 24, then $12 + 4 + z + 6 = 24$.
    Therefore $z = 2$.
    The line $8 + y + z + 9 = 24$.
    When $z = 2$, $y = 5$.

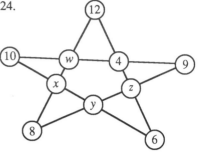

10. Solution 1
    In order to get an equal number of 5 kg and 2 kg bags, he could first divide the
    potatoes into 7 kg units.
    The number of 7 kg units would be $126 \div 7 = 18$.
    Thus there would be 18 five kg units and 18 two kg units.
    The number of bags used was $18 + 18 = 36$.

    Solution 2
    Let the number of 2 kg bags be n.
    Their total weight would be $2(n) = 2n$ kg.
    The number of 5 kg bags would also be n.
    Their total weight would be $5(n) = 5n$ kg.
    Hence $2n + 5n = 126$
    $$7n = 126$$
    $$n = 18$$
    The number of bags used was $18 + 18 = 36$.

11. Solution
    When a piece of cheese is given by one mouse to another, the difference in the number
    of pieces that each has changes by 2. (One total goes up by 1, the other down by 1).
    From the first statement, we deduce that one mouse has exactly two more pieces of
    cheese that the other.
    From the second statement, if the mouse with two fewer pieces gave one piece to the
    other mouse, the difference in the number of pieces would be 4.
    The only numbers that differ by 4, such that the larger number is double the smaller
    number, are 8 and 4.
    Hence the total number of pieces is $8 + 4 = 12$.
    (The actual numbers of pieces they started with were 5 and 7).

12. <u>Solution 1</u>

    If the coins are all dimes, only $9 \times 10 = 90$ cents is obtained.

    If the coins are all quarters, $9 \times 25 = 225$ cents is obtained.

    If a quarter replaces a dime an increase of 15 cents results.

    If only dimes are used, $135 - 90 = 45$ cents are lacking.

    Hence from the nine dimes, three replacements of dimes with quarters will be necessary.

    Hence we need 6 dimes and 3 quarters, since $6 \times 10 + 3 \times 25 = 135$.

    On the other hand, if only quarters are used, the nine quarters or 225 cents produces $225 - 135 = 90$ cents surplus.

    Therefore we need to replace $\frac{90}{15} = 6$ quarters with dimes.

    Therefore we need $9 - 6 = 3$ quarters and 6 dimes.

    <u>Solution 2</u>

    Let the number of quarters be x.

    Then the number of dimes is $9 - x$.

    The value of the quarters is $25x$ cents.

    The value of the dimes is $10(9 - x)$ cents.

    Therefore $\quad 25x + 10(9 - x) = 135$
    $$25x + 90 - 10x = 135$$
    $$15x = 45$$
    $$x = 3$$

    Then 3 quarters and 6 dimes are used.

13. <u>Solution</u>

    The number of coins that may be placed along the width of the sheet is $6 \div \frac{3}{4} = 8$.

    The number of coins that may be placed along the length of the sheet is $12 \div \frac{3}{4} = 16$.

    Therefore the maximum number of coins that can be placed on the sheet, with no overlapping or overhanging is $8 \times 16 = 128$.

14. <u>Solution 1</u>

    If the people are put in order, the first person will shake hands with each of the remaining five. Then the next person will shake hands with the four he has not met yet. The next person will shake hands with the remaining three others, and so on, until the second last person shakes hands with the last person.

    Hence the number of handshakes is $5 + 4 + 3 + 2 + 1 = 15$.

Solution 2

If the persons were A, B, C, D, E, and F, the answer is just the number of sides and diagonals of a hexagon. Since from any vertex there are 5 outgoing lines, then the total number of joining lines is $6 \times 5 = 30$. However each of these has been counted twice since joining A to E is the same as joining E to A. Hence the number of joining lines (or the number of handshakes) is $30 \div 2 = 15$.

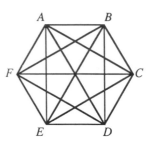

15. Solution

Since 4 students belong to neither club, there are 29 students who belong to the mathematics club, the science club, or to both clubs.

The number belonging to the mathematics club, or the science club, or both is $18 + 17 = 35$.

But since there are only 29 members in total the number belonging to both clubs is $35 - 29 = 6$.

16. Solution

Since 60 poles are needed, they could be cut from 60 different 16 unit poles. Of course, this would not be the least number required.

Since ten poles, 10 units long are required, these must be cut from *ten* 16 unit poles. This cutting also provides ten of the 6 unit poles needed.

The remaining twenty 6 unit poles and twenty 8 unit poles may be obtained from an additional *twenty* 16 unit poles.

This may be done by cutting ten 16 unit poles in half, thus creating the twenty 8 unit poles and then cutting two 6 unit poles from each of the ten other 16 unit poles, or by cutting a 6 unit pole and an 8 unit pole from each 16 unit pole. There is, of course, some wastage.

No matter how you cut them, the least number of 16 unit poles required is 30.

3-Dimensional Geometry - I

Multiple Choice Questions

1. Solution
    Opposite faces of a cube are parallel.
    There are three pairs of parallel faces.
    The answer is B.

    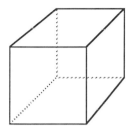

2. Solution
    Since 10 mm is equivalent to 1 cm, the dimensions
    of the block, in cm, are 0.12 by 0.10 by 0.08.

    The volume of the block, in cm³, is

    length × width × height = 0.12 × 0.10 × 0.08
    $$= 0.96.$$

    The answer is Ĉ.

    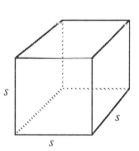

3. Solution
    Let each edge of the cube have length s cm.
    Thus, $s \times s \times s = 64$ or $s^3 = 64$.
    Hence, $s = 4$.
    The six faces each have dimensions 4 cm by 4 cm.
    Each face has area 16 cm².
    The total surface area of the cube is
    $6 \times 16 = 96$ cm².
    The answer is C.

    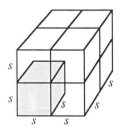

4. Solution
    Let the length of each edge of the original cube be s.
    Thus, the length of each edge of the larger cube is $2s$.
    The volume of the original cube is s^3.
    The volume of the larger cube is $(2s)^3 = 8s^3$.
    Therefore it requires 8 original cubes to fill the larger
    cube.
    The answer is D.

5. Solution

Since R is folded over first, it will be completely covered by flaps Q and S when they are folded. Finally, since P is folded over last, the appearance from the top is

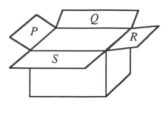

X

The answer is A.

6. Solution

A backhoe can dig a hole of volume 27 m³ in one hour.

A hole of volume 6^3 m³ can be dug by a backhoe in $6^3 \div 27 = 8$ hours. Two backhoes could complete the job in 4 hours.

The answer is C.

7. Solution

Each of the small cubes that contains any part of an edge of the original block will have more than one red face.

The only unit cubes having exactly one red face will be those formed from the interior of the original faces.

There are two such cubes from each of the 3 by 4 faces of the original block.

Hence, the total is 4.

The answer is B.

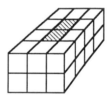

8. Solution

Removing the cube marked K decreases the original surface area by 2 cm² since two of the original 1 cm by 1 cm faces have been removed. But four "inner" 1 cm by 1 cm faces have now been exposed and form part of the surface.

The net increase in surface area is 2 cm².

The answer is A.

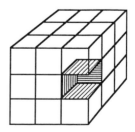

9. Solution

The largest cylinder that will fit inside a 10 cm by 10 cm by 10 cm cube will have height 10 cm and a circular base of diameter 10 cm.

The area of its base is

$$A = \pi r^2$$
$$= \pi(5)^2$$
$$= 25\pi \text{ cm}^2$$

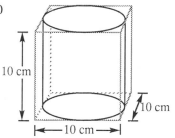

The volume of the cylinder is

$$V = \text{(area of base)(height of cylinder)}$$
$$= (25\pi)(10)$$
$$= 250\pi \text{ cm}^3$$

The answer is C.

10. Solution

Fold the four sides out so that they are in the same plane as the top.

The shortest distance for the ant is the straight line distance from A to B.

There are two cases to consider since the ant could proceed along AB or along $A'B$.

AB is the hypotenuse of right-angled triangle ABC.

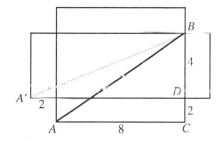

Thus $AB = \sqrt{8^2 + 6^2}$
$= 10$

$A'B$ is the hypotenuse of right-angled triangle $A'BD$.

Hence, $A'B = \sqrt{10^2 + 4^2}$
$= \sqrt{116}$

The shortest distance from A to B, along the surface of the block is 10.

The answer is E.

11. Solution 1

When punching out the designated columns from front to back, 25 of the smaller cubes are removed. When punching out the designated columns from top to bottom, the number of smaller cubes removed from each level are 5, 1, 4, 1, and 5, respectively. When punching out the designated columns from side to side, the

number of smaller cubes removed from each level are 5, 1, 4, 1, and 5 respectively.
The total number of smaller cubes removed is 25 + 16 + 16 = 57, leaving
125 – 57 = 68 cubes.

Solution 2

After all the designated columns have been punched out, the five layers, from front to
back, as drawn, illustrate the number of smaller cubes remaining.

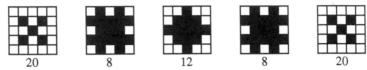

Thus, the total number of smaller cubes remaining is 20 + 8 + 12 + 8 + 20 = 68 cubes.
The answer is D.

12. Solution

The original volume is *rst*.

The new volumes possible are

$(r + 1)st = rst + st$

$r(s + 1)t = rst + rt$

$rs(t + 1) = rst + rs$

Since $r < s < t$, then $rst + st$ is the greatest.

The answer is A.

Full Solution Questions

1. Solution

In the diagram, there are three edges on each of the
top and bottom faces. There are three vertical
edges.

The total number of edges is 9.

2. Solution

The bottom requires 10 + 15 = 25 cm.

The top also requires 25 cm.

The four sides require 4 × 20 = 80 cm.

The bow requires 47 cm.

The total length of ribbon required is
25 + 25 + 80 + 47 = 177 cm.

or 1.77 m.

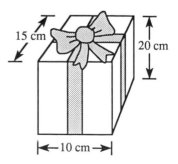

3. <u>Solution</u>

Let the length, width, and height of the original box
be *l* cm, *w* cm, and *h* cm, respectively.

Thus, its volume is $lwh = 15$ cm^3.

The volume of the box having dimensions double
those of the given box is

$$(2l)(2w)(2h) = 8lwh$$
$$= 8(15)$$
$$= 120 \text{ cm}^3.$$

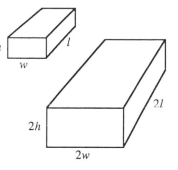

4. <u>Solution</u>

In order to have paint on exactly two faces, the
small cube must contain part of an edge of the
original cube but not one of its 8 vertices.
The middle cube on each edge has this property.
Since the original cube has 12 edges, there will be
12 unit cubes with exactly two faces painted red.

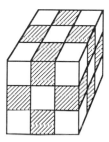

5. <u>Solution</u>

The original square piece of cardboard has
dimensions 6 cm by 6 cm.

By removing squares of 1 cm^2 from each corner,
the base of the box is a square of size 4 cm by 4 cm.
The height of the box is 1 cm.

The volume of the box is $4 \times 4 \times 1 = 16$ cm^3.

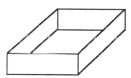

6. Solution
    A diagram is always helpful in solving
    problems of this type. The difficulty is in
    drawing a two dimensional figure that shows
    all six faces.

    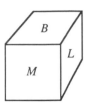

    The second diagram shown is one way to do
    so. *B* and *C* represent the top and bottom
    of the cube and *K*, *L*, *M*, and *N* represent
    the other four faces.
    From this diagram, it is seen that only
    opposite faces of a cube do not have any
    edges in common. Hence, opposite faces can
    be the same colour. Therefore, the minimum
    number of colours required to paint the cube
    is three.

    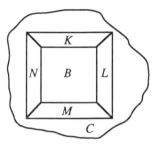

7. Solution
    The largest sphere will touch all six faces of the box.
    The diameter of the sphere is 6.
    Hence, the radius of the sphere is 3.
    The volume of this sphere is
    $V = \frac{4}{3}\pi(3)^3 = 36\pi.$

    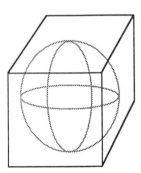

    Cross - section

    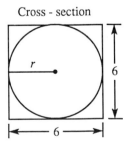

8. <u>Solution</u>

The volume of water in the tank is $4 \times 4 \times 3 = 48$ cu. ft.

Placing the solid cube in the tank is equivalent to adding 8 cu. ft. of water to the tank.

The volume of the tank being occupied is 56 cu. ft.

If h ft. is the new height, then

$$4 \times 4 \times h = 56$$
$$h = \frac{56}{16}$$
$$= 3.5$$

The new height of the water is 3.5 feet.

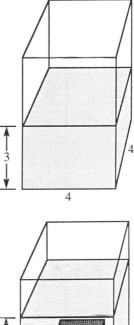

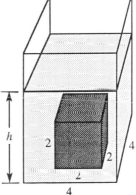

9. <u>Solution</u>

The bottom requires $10 \times 10 = 100$ cubes.

The construction of each additional layer of the four sides requires $2 \times 10 + 2 \times 8 = 36$ cubes.

Since there are nine layers above the base, the total number of cubes required is $100 + (9 \times 36) = 424$.

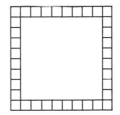

10. <u>Solution</u>

Since the width, 60 cm, is the same for both
positions of the tank, only the cross-sectional areas
need be considered.

In the tipped position, the cross-section of the water
is the right-angled triangle ADC. Since $AD = 40$
cm and $AC = 50$ cm, the area of $\triangle ADC$ is
$\frac{1}{2}(40)(50) = 1000$ cm^2.

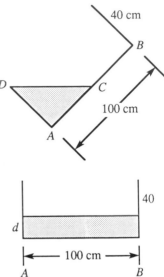

Let d cm be the depth of the water when the tank is
returned to a horizontal position. The cross-section
of the water is a rectangle with dimensions d cm by
100 cm.

The area of this rectangle is $100d$ cm^2.

Since the volume of water has not changed, the two
cross-sectional areas must be equal.

Thus, $100d = 1000$

$$d = 10$$

The depth of the water is 10 cm when the tank is in
the horizontal position.

11. <u>Solution</u>

If the sum of the numbers on three of the faces is 15, the numbers are 4, 5, and 6.
If the sum of the numbers on three of the faces is 14, the numbers are 3, 5, and 6.
There are two cases to consider. In each case both the 5 and 6 must be visible from
two positions.

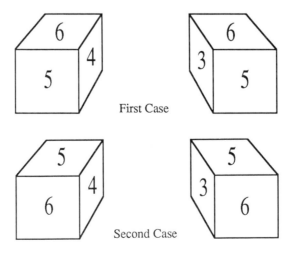

First Case

Second Case

If the 6 is on the top (Case 1), then 1 and 2 must be on the sides to give a sum of 9. This is not possible since three of the four sides are already allocated to 3, 4, and 5. Hence, the number on the top is 5 (Case 2) and 1 is on the fourth side since $5 + 3 + 1 = 9$.

Therefore the bottom number is 2.

12. <u>Solution</u>

The required section, $ABCD$, is a tetrahedron.

The volume of a tetrahedron is

$V = \frac{1}{3}$(area of base)(height).

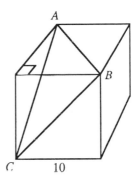

Any one of the triangles ABD, ADC, BDC, and ABC can be considered as base, but using $\triangle ABC$ makes the problem much more difficult than is necessary.

The area of base $\triangle ABD$ is $\frac{1}{2} \times 10 \times 10 = 50$.

The height of the tetrahedron from this base is 10.

Therefore the volume of the smaller section is

$V = \frac{1}{3}(50)(10) = 166\frac{2}{3}$.

Challenge Problems

Multiple Choice Questions

1. <u>Solution</u>

   Two numbers whose sum is 11 and whose product is 24 are 8 and 3.

   Their reciprocals are $\frac{1}{8}$ and $\frac{1}{3}$.

   The sum of these reciprocals is $\frac{1}{8} + \frac{1}{3} = \frac{3}{24} + \frac{8}{24}$

   $$= \frac{11}{24}.$$

   The answer is B.

2. <u>Solution</u>

   To assess the properties of the given choices the operations must be performed.

   The sum of 6 and 12 is 18. Their product is $6 \times 12 = 72$. $72 \div 18 = 4$.

       Therefore the sum is a factor of the product.

   The sum of 5 and 10 is 15. Their product is $5 \times 10 = 50$. $50 \div 15 = 3\frac{1}{3}$.

       The sum is not a factor of the product.

   The sum of 4 and 8 is 12. Their product is $4 \times 8 = 32$. $32 \div 12 = 2\frac{2}{3}$.

       The sum is not a factor of the product.

   The sum of 2 and 4 is 6. Their product is $2 \times 4 = 8$. $8 \div 6 = 1\frac{1}{3}$.

       The sum is not a factor of the product.

   The sum of 1 and 2 is 3. Their product is $1 \times 2 = 2$. $2 \div 3 = \frac{2}{3}$.

       The sum is not a factor of the product.

   The numbers 6 and 12 have the required property.

   The answer is A.

3. <u>Solution</u>

   The horizontal segment is *CD*.

   C and *D* are the only points with the same second
   coordinates.

   The answer is D.

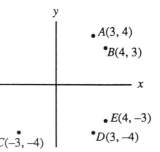

4. Solution
   Testing the given numbers we find
   $$5 - 5^2 = 5 - 25 = -20$$
   $$1 - 1^2 = 1 - 1 = 0$$
   $$\frac{1}{2} - \left(\frac{1}{2}\right)^2 = \frac{1}{2} - \frac{1}{4} = \frac{1}{4}$$
   $$\frac{1}{10} - \left(\frac{1}{10}\right)^2 = \frac{1}{10} - \frac{1}{100} = \frac{9}{100}$$
   $$-5 - (-5)^2 = -5 - 25 = -30$$
   The greatest result is $\frac{1}{4}$ which occurs when the number is $\frac{1}{2}$.
   The answer is C.

5. Solution
   Since the product is negative, one integer is negative and the other is positive.
   Listing the possibilities of pairs of integers whose product is –24, we have
   (1, –24), (2, –12), (3, –8), (4, –6), (6, –4), (8, –3), (12, –2), (24, –1).
   From this group we see that $(-8) - 3 = -11$.
   Therefore the pair is (3, –8) and their sum is $-8 + 3 = -5$.
   The answer is D.

6. Solution
   If the area of rectangle $AEHG$ is 21 cm^2 and the length and width are integers, the
   dimensions must be 7 cm × 3 cm or 21 cm × 1 cm.
   The dimensions of rectangle $HJCF$ must be 7 cm × 4 cm or 14 cm × 2 cm or
   28 cm × 1 cm.
   Since $GHFD$ is a square, GH and HF must be equal.
   From the above dimensions, $GH = HF = 1$ cm, or $GH = HF = 7$ cm.
   Therefore, a possible area is $7 \times 7 = 49$ cm^2 or $1 \times 1 = 1$ cm^2.
   Only one of these answers is listed.
   The answer is A.

7. Solution
   The two integers with a sum of –4 and a product of –21 are 3 and –7.
   The greater of these two integers is 3.
   The answer is D.

8. Solution
   The correct change that Tina should receive was $20.00 – $13.98 = $6.02.
   Tina, however, received $13.98.
   Therefore Tina should return $13.98 – $6.02 = $7.96.
   The answer is C.

9. Solution

    To determine the elapsed time, we must count the time intervals between the strikings. In timing the 6 o'clock strikings, there are 5 intervals.

    The elapsed time for 5 intervals is 5 seconds, so each interval lasts one second.

    The 12 strokes at 12 o'clock require 11 intervals, so they take 11 seconds.

    The answer is E.

10. Solution 1

    Let $m = \frac{a}{b}$ and $n = \frac{c}{d}$ be fractions between 0 and 1.

    Thus $a < b$ and $c < d$; and $ac < bd$.

    Therefore $m \times n = \frac{a}{b} \times \frac{c}{d} = \frac{ac}{bd} < 1$.

    Solution 2

    In a question of this type, some answers can be eliminated by using a counterexample.

    If $m = \frac{3}{4}$ and $n = \frac{1}{2}$, then $m + n = \frac{5}{4} > 1$, so answer B is not always true.

    If $m = \frac{3}{4}$ and $n = \frac{1}{2}$, then $\frac{m}{n} = \frac{3}{4} \div \frac{1}{2} = \frac{3}{4} \times \frac{2}{1} = \frac{3}{2} > 1$, so answer C is not always true.

    If $m = \frac{1}{4}$ and $n = \frac{1}{2}$, then $m + n = \frac{1}{4} + \frac{1}{2} = \frac{3}{4} < 1$, so answer D is not always true.

    If $m = \frac{1}{4}$ and $n = \frac{1}{2}$, then $m^2 + n^2 = \frac{1}{16} + \frac{1}{4} = \frac{5}{16} < 1$, so answer E is not always true.

    Therefore $m \times n < 1$ is the only answer possible.

    The answer is A.

11. Solution

    If the team never won more than 5 games in a row, then the maximum number of games they could have won would occur when every five wins was followed by a loss.

    Thus they won 5 out of every 6 games or $\frac{5}{6}$ of 180 = 150 games.

    Thus they could not win more than 150 games.

    The answer is D.

    Note: It is interesting to note that the minimum number of games won would have occurred by following three losses with a win.

    The team would then win only 1 out of every 4 games played, or $\frac{1}{4}$ of 180 = 45 games.

    Under the conditions stated, the team could have won as few as 45 games or as many as 150 games, in a season of 180 games.

    The team could have won any number of games from 45 to 150 inclusive.

12. <u>Solution 1</u>

In questions of this type it is probably best to list the numbers with one property and then check for the second property.

The numbers which are less than 100 and are multiples of 6 are 6, 12, 18, 24, 30, 36, 42, 48, 54, 60, 66, 72, 78, 84, 90, and 96.

Of these, those that end in 4 are 24, 54, and 84.

Hence the sum is 24 + 54 + 84 = 162.

Note: One could also list the numbers ending in 4: 4, 14, 24, 34, 44, 54, 64, 74, 84, 94.

Now testing those which are multiples of 6 we find 24, 54, and 84.

<u>Solution 2</u>

To end in 4 the numbers must differ by 10, 20, 30, 40, etc.

The only one of these numbers which is a multiple of 6 is 30.

Hence when you find one number, the others will differ by 30.

Once 24 is found, the only other numbers are 24 + 30 = 54, and 54 + 30 = 84.

The sum of all such numbers is 24 + 54 + 84 = 162.

The answer is A.

13. <u>Solution</u>

If A and B represent the two boys and M and N represent the two men, the nine crossings required are illustrated below.

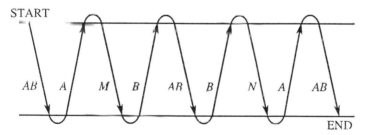

The answer is E.

14. <u>Solution</u>

In order to calculate speeds we must always consider the distance covered in a certain time.

Driving at 30 m.p.h. for 1 mile requires $\frac{1}{30}$ of an hour or 2 minutes.

To average 60 m.p.h. for 2 miles requires $\frac{2}{60}$ of an hour or 2 minutes.

Therefore the car has to drive the second mile in 0 minutes, which, of course, is impossible.

The answer is E.

15. <u>Solution</u>

If $(xy)^2 = xyz$ then $(xy)(xy) = xyz$.

Dividing by xy (since x and y are not zero) gives $xy = z$.

There are an infinite number of solutions to this equation.

However we only have to test the given choices.

If $z = 1$, then $xy = 1$, so $x = 1$, $y = 1$. Since the numbers cannot be the same, this is rejected.

If $z = 5$, then $xy = 5$, so x and y are 1 and 5 or 5 and 1. Two of the numbers are the same so this is rejected.

If $z = 9$, then $xy = 9$, so $(x, y) = (3, 3)$, $(1, 9)$, or $(9, 1)$. In any case two of the digits are the same, so this is rejected.

If $z = 11$, then $xy = 11$, so $(x, y) = (1, 11)$ or $(11, 1)$. Two of the digits are the same so this is rejected.

If $z = 16$, then $xy = 16$, so $(x, y) = (1, 16)$, $(2, 8)$, $(4, 4)$, $(8, 2)$, or $(16, 1)$. Only one set of possible values emerges, namely $z = 16$ and $(x, y) = (2, 8)$ or $(8, 2)$.

The answer is E.

Full Solution Questions

1. <u>Solution</u>

Two positive integers with a sum of 7 and a product of 12 are 3 and 4.

The sum of their squares is $3^2 + 4^2 = 9 + 16$

$$= 25.$$

2. <u>Solution</u>

Make a line diagram, placing the towns according to the directions given and we find the following.

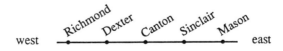

The town which is farthest west is Richmond.

3. <u>Solution</u>

Since the thousands digit is 7 times the tens digit, the tens digit must be 1. The tens digit cannot be 0 or the thousands digit would be 0. It cannot be 2 or greater since this would result in a two-digit thousands digit, which is impossible.

Since the hundreds digit and the tens digit have a sum of 2, the hundreds digit must be 1, since $1 + 1 = 2$.

The thousands digit must be $7 \times 1 = 7$.

The units digit is 5 more than the hundreds digit so must be $5 + 1 = 6$.

Therefore the number is 7116.

4. Solution

The number cannot be negative, since its square root would not be a real number.

The square of a positive number larger than 1 is always larger than the number.

Since the sum is fairly large (276) the square must be near this number.

We only need to check numbers whose squares are slightly less than 276.

We note that $15^2 = 225$.

Testing $a + a^2 + \sqrt{a}$ where a is 15 gives $15 + 225 + \sqrt{15} \neq 276$.

Testing 16, $a + a^2 + \sqrt{a}$ gives $16 + 256 + 4 = 276$.

The number is 16.

5. Solution

The dog will gain $9 - 7 = 2$ metres for every 9 metres that it runs.

To gain the 160 metres, the dog must run $\frac{160}{2}$ intervals.

To gain the 160 metres it must run $\frac{160}{2} \times 9 = 720$ metres.

6. Solution

A full load is 6 Pintos and 7 Toyotas or 8 Pintos and 4 Toyotas.

Hence if 2 extra Pintos are added then 3 Toyotas must be removed.

In the load of 6 Pintos and 7 Toyotas, we want to remove the 6 Pintos and replace them with 9 Toyotas, since every 2 Pintos occupy the same space as 3 Toyotas.

The maximum load would be $7 + 9 = 16$ Toyotas.

7. Solution

To find the next palindrome we must make the least increase as possible. This will be accomplished, with a number having an odd number of digits, by increasing the middle digit by 1.

For example, the next palindrome after 131 is 141, and the next palindrome after 191 is 202.

In the last example we had to change the outer digits since the middle digit became 0.

In a number having an even number of digits we would increase each of the two internal digits by 1.

For example, the next palindrome after 2772 is 2882, and the next palindrome after 2992 is 3003.

To change 15951 to the next palindrome we would change the 9 to 0 and make the other changes necessary.

Thus the next palindrome after 15951 is 16061.

The increase is 16061 − 15951 = 110 miles.

8. Solution 1

    Four cats and three kittens weigh 44 kg.

    Three cats and two kittens weigh 32 kg.

    By subtraction, one cat and one kitten weigh 12 kg, so that two cats and two kittens weigh 24 kg.

    Using the fact that three cats and two kittens weigh 32 kg, we learn that one cat weighs 32 − 24 = 8 kg and thus one kitten weighs 4 kg.

    Therefore the weight of two cats and one kitten is 2(8) + 4 = 20 kg.

    Solution 2

    From the second statement we know that six cats and four kittens weigh 64 kg.

    But four cats and three kittens weigh 44 kg.

    By subtracting, two cats and one kitten weigh 64 − 44 = 20 kg.

9. Solution

    The greatest value of y will occur when x is least, namely 0.

    When $x = 0$, then $y = 8$ which is a solution.

    The greatest value of x will occur when y is least, namely 0.

    When $y = 0$, then $x = 12$ which is a solution.

    We must test values of x between 0 and 12.

    We find other ordered pairs, namely (3, 6), (6, 4), and (9, 2).

    There are 5 such ordered pairs that satisfy this equation.

    Note: When you discover one solution set (in this problem), another set is found by increasing the x value by 3 and decreasing the y value by 2.

10. Solution

    The number of one-digit numbers from 1 to 9 is 9.

    The number of two-digit numbers from 10 to 99 is 90.

    The number of three-digit numbers from 100 to 250 is 151.

    Therefore the number of digits required is $(9 \times 1) + (90 \times 2) + (151 \times 3)$
    $$= 9 + 180 + 453$$
    $$= 642.$$

11. Solution

    The two-digit squares are 16, 25, 36, 49, 64, and 81.
    The three-digit squares are 100, 121, 144, 169, 196, 225, 256, 289, 324, 361, 400, 441, 484, 529, 576, 625, 676, 729, 784, 841, 900, and 961.
    By comparing the two lists we find that:

    by inserting a 9 between 1 and 6 we get $196 = 14^2$,

    by inserting a 2 between 2 and 5 we get $225 = 15^2$,

    by inserting a 4 between 8 and 1 we get $841 = 29^2$.

    There are three numbers with the required property.

12. Solution

    Suppose the father's age is x years.
    Then the son's age is $(33 - x)$ years.
    In T years their ages will be $x + T$ and $T + 33 - x$ years.

    $x + T = 4(T + 33 - x)$
    $x + T = 4T + 132 - 4x$

    $5x - 3T = 132$

    There are many solutions to this equation, but since we want the smallest value for T, we will test, starting with $T = 1$.
    If $T = 1$, $5x - 3 = 132$

    $5x = 135$
    $x = 27$.

    The present ages are 27 and 6 years.
    In 1 year, their ages will be 28 and 7 years.
    Therefore in 1 year the father will be 4 times as old as his son.

13. Solution

    Since $ABCD$ is a rectangle, $AD = BC = 12$.
    Therefore $BE = 12 + 1 = 13$.
    Therefore radius $BD = BE = 13$.

    By the Pythagorean Theorem, $BD^2 = AB^2 + AD^2$

    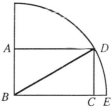

    $13^2 = AB^2 + 12^2$
    $AB^2 = 13^2 - 12^2$
    $= 169 - 144$
    $= 25$

    Therefore $AB = 5$.